Animals and Their Ways

J. D. CARTHY

Animals and Their Ways

The Science of Animal Behavior

Nature and Science Library

published for

The American Museum of Natural History

by The Natural History Press / Garden City, New York

First published in the United States of America in 1965 by
The Natural History Press, Garden City, New York
in association with Aldus Books Limited

Library of Congress Catalog Card No. 65-12164
© Aldus Books Limited, London, 1965

Printed in Italy by Arnoldo Mondadori, Verona

Contents

Our knowledge about the behavior of animals comes mainly from careful observation of their activities. From this photograph we can learn two important facts about this bullfrog. First, it preys upon the monarch butterfly. Second, it often catches its prey while the monarch is in flight. We may also make a logical guess that it recognizes the monarch by its flight movements and, possibly, by the color of its wings.

1. What Is Behavior?

A cat stalking a blackbird crouches close to the ground, then shuffles its feet back and forth to prepare itself for a sudden spring at its prey. Meanwhile, the blackbird shows its awareness of danger by calling in staccato, rattling phrases that develop into rapid, high-pitched chirping sounds. Both cat and bird are displaying obvious examples of animal behavior—in this case hunting and alarm behavior respectively. There are many less obvious examples. For instance when certain animals, including humans, are hungry and smell food, glands in their cheeks and under their tongues produce saliva. This, too, is an example of behavior; it displays an animal's readiness to eat.

Behavior, then, can be defined simply as the response of an organism to its environment. Every form of behavior, whether simple or complex, is a reaction to *stimuli*. A stimulus is usually a change in some aspect of an organism's environment. Stimuli may be complex, like the sound of a symphony on a record; or simple, like the sound of the phonograph needle touching a small scratch on the same record.

If a person knew something about music he could probably explain in some detail why he liked (or disliked) the symphony. He could also explain why he disliked the scratching of the needle. Man is the only species of animal that has the ability to describe stimuli, to analyze his response to them—and to communicate detailed information about both to his fellows. With other animals no "inside information" of this kind is available. Our study and interpretation of their behavior depends largely upon careful observation of their physical movements.

We know that an animal is receiving stimuli by its actions, either through shifts of the whole body or by the movement of some part of it. A dog lying curled up, seemingly fast asleep, will cock its ear at a noise. That is, it will respond to the stimulus of sound. All responses to stimuli involve the action of muscles of some sort (in this case, those controlling the dog's ear); muscles are called effectors, and are part of the *effector system* which also includes glands.

Not all stimuli come from outside the animal. As we shall see later, some arise from within the body itself. In man such stimuli rarely come to the attention of the conscious mind but nevertheless they affect our behavior in definite ways.

A stimulus may operate indirectly by becoming linked, through experience, with a particular action or object. Dogs, for example, learn to respond when their food plate is rattled with a spoon. The rattling sound is a signal—or *token stimulus*—for the food that is to come. We know that honey bees are attracted to flowers through their scent, but it is the nectar in the blossom that bees are after. Token stimuli of this sort may be as important a source of animal behavior as those that come directly from the food, other animals, or objects with which they have become associated.

The Environment

Stimuli come from both living and non-living parts of an animal's environment, and they are both physical and chemical in nature. Light, heat, sound, and pressure are some of the physical sources of stimuli common to most surroundings. Plants and other animals are the main source of chemical stimuli. Light from the sun (an inanimate part of the surroundings), for example, may be reflected off one living creature to produce an image in the eye of another that is observing it. Or the light may be simpler in its effect, merely causing an animal to move away from (or toward) it, as when an insect scurries into the shadow cast by a stone.

Colored light may cause different results from white light. If the eye of the animal is able to form a sharp image the animal may learn to recognize — and thus respond in different ways to — specific shapes. If the eye is able also to distinguish between different colors, the behavior of the animal will be influenced in yet other ways. To birds and bees, particularly, color and shape are important stimuli to behavior. Clearly, behavior varies greatly in different animals, depending among other things upon the development of their sense organs.

In human beings, light is an especially important source of stimulation because vision is the best developed of our senses. We are essentially "seeing" animals. But this is not true of all other animals, many of which rely far more on the special sensitivity of one or more of their other senses.

Sound, for example, is important to most animals, particularly when it comes from another animal, of either their own or a different species. It may signify food, or danger, or some other aspect of the environment equally important to the animal. The male grass-

A simple response to a stimulus: Euglena, a microscopic pond organism, moves toward light. It has no eye, but a light-sensitive pigment spot at the front of its body guides it toward a source of light. The organism swims in spiral movements by means of a whip-like appendage at its front end.

Although horses have a keen sense of smell, they seem to rely on vision for identifying others of their species. In this experiment the horse in the upper picture "recognized" the horse in the photograph, while the foal in the lower picture adopted the typical feeding position alongside the photograph of a mare.

hopper calls its mate by making a chirping sound. A male bird warns other males off his "territory" by a special song, and when a baby howler monkey falls out of a tree it makes a particular sound to summon its mother. These three examples show that sound is important in keeping animals together, whether as mating pairs or as family groups.

Humans think of sound mainly as that of voices, or musical instruments, or machines. Sound comes to us as waves carried in air. But some animals are particularly sensitive to vibrations that reach them through objects or through the ground. The struggles of an insect caught in a spider's web make the strands of the web vibrate. The spider receives this information through its legs which are resting on the strands.

We know that the shape and texture of objects can be detected by the sense of touch. Blindfolded, we have no difficulty in distin-

Sound is important to most animals, especially in helping them to recognize other animals. Frogs produce sound by forcing air out of special sacs. The large size sacs of the European edible frog add resonance to the frog's voice.

We usually associate vocal organs with the throat, but the sound-producing organs of many insects are located elsewhere. In the cicada (left), for instance, they are at the front of the abdomen (see area shown in blue). The cicada "sings" by vibrating two membranes, one on either side of its body, by means of a pair of large muscles (above) that lie within the abdomen wall.

The antennae of this moon moth is sensitive to smell. Some male insects are capable of scenting females at distances of up to half a mile.

At the onset of winter the lives of hibernating animals, such as this chipmunk, depend on their sensitivity to climatic changes. Their perception of the gradually decreasing length of day and of the fall in temperature prompts them to hole up in warm burrows, where they remain until the following spring.

guishing whether we have been handed a stone or an apple. When combined with sensitivity to chemicals, the touch sense can provide somewhat the same kind of information that a colored visual image brings to the eye. We associate scent with our noses, which breathe in streams of air containing very diluted chemicals, and we associate taste with our mouths or tongues and the chemicals in food and drink that touch them. But many insects taste chemicals through sense organs in their feet, and smell objects through their antennae that wave in the air.

To an animal, scent and taste play as important a part as vision does for humans. The smell of certain oils in plants makes them either attractive or repellent to insect larvae, for example. And the scent left by mammals marks their claim to an area as surely as song fixes the "territory" of a bird. Scents, whether those of mammals or bees living in a colony, are the means by which animals identify each other.

Temperature is one of the physical factors of the environment, and sensitivity to it may determine whether or not an animal survives. If the temperature rises too high or falls too low, the animal may die. In some places temperatures vary widely. For example, in a desert the sand gets so hot during the day that many animals, such as desert rats and lizards, burrow to the cooler layers beneath and emerge

only at night. On the other hand, some cold-blooded animals need warmth before they can move about easily. Locusts, at first light of morning, are too cold to fly. They arrange themselves broadside to the sun, tilting their bodies in order to absorb as much heat as possible. Later, when the sun is hot and they are warmed, they turn to face its rays, exposing their bodies as little as possible. Locusts have heat receptors, arranged on their heads and along their bodies, that are able to take in heat in much the same way as our eyes take in light.

Few animals seem deliberately to avoid cold temperatures. The warm-blooded animals can adjust to extremes of climate, but cold-blooded animals suffer in these conditions. When the temperature drops sharply many of them are overcome by a cold stupor and lose their ability to move out of their surroundings long before they are finally frozen stiff.

Warm-blooded animals, such as birds and mammals, are often hosts to parasitic creatures that live on their skin among the feathers or hair. To parasites such as ticks and lice, temperature is vital. It is by sensing the body warmth of the host that they are able to find their food supply. Many years ago the presence of lice on a man's body used to be considered a mark of health, for it was known that lice will leave a body that is suffering

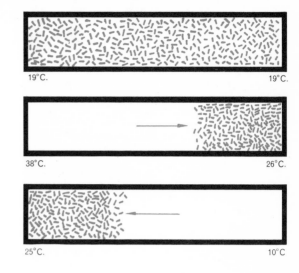

The single-cell paramecium, a microscopic pond animal, is very sensitive to heat and cold. The diagrams above show how paramecia behave in troughs of water at various temperatures. In the two lower troughs the animals have moved toward areas nearest 26°C., the environmental temperature at which their body chemistry functions best.

The internal temperature of cold-blooded animals, such as this British grass snake, fluctuates with that of their environment. Extreme cold slows down the activities of cold-blooded animals to the point where they may not be able to move.

Plants, too, react to stimuli. The tentacles of the common sundew trap a house fly as soon as it touches the plant. The tentacles are then stimulated to release a sticky solution over the fly, which is digested within half an hour.

from fever, as the host's temperature goes up.

The ability to respond to stimuli is a necessary property of all living things. Plants, too, "behave" in the sense that they react to changes in their environment. Compared with the more obvious movements of animals, the responses of plants are slow and almost imperceptible. Since plant reactions are mainly growth movements, they are of a passive or fixed kind, whereas those of animals are active and variable. If a growing plant bends toward the light, its stem will remain bent at that point even if the light moves to another position. But an animal is able to stay or leave the light, and shows no structural changes from exposure to it. One of the few plants that does display reversible behavior is the mimosa. When touched, its leaves collapse; then, after a time, they recover and are once again able

to react. Other plants, like the single-celled algae, can swim about actively and in their limited way do respond to their surroundings in somewhat the same way as an animal. But these are exceptions to the normally passive behavior of plants.

Interpreting Behavior

The behavior of many animals is highly complex and is often difficult to interpret. Nevertheless an animal's response to a given situation is limited by its physical structure and the level of development of its nervous system. In other words its behavior is governed largely by the revolutionary processes that have shaped the species to which it belongs. It is important to remember this when we try to understand the behavior of any ani-

*In calling his painting "Dignity and Impudence,"
Sir Edwin Landseer ascribed human emotions to
animals. The awareness in animals of such essentially
human concepts as dignity and impudence is
extremely unlikely.*

mal. We are often tempted to put ourselves in
the animal's place and interpret its behavior
in terms of our own feelings and reactions. If
an animal cowers when it is touched, we may
be correct in assuming that it is frightened.
But we are not justified in assuming that it
must feel the same sensations that we do when
we are afraid. Ascribing human emotions to
other animals is termed *anthropomorphism*. It
is unscientific and it can be misleading. There
is no way by which we can look into an animal's mind to determine the precise nature of
its feelings, nor can anthropomorphic as-
sumptions be tested by experiment, which is
fundamental to scientific method. True, an
animal may behave "sensibly"—that is, in
the way a human might behave under similar
circumstances. But it often happens that the
animal will continue to behave in the same

way under radically altered circumstances,
even though its behavior, now, is "unsuitable"
in human terms and may even be dangerous
to itself. Most animals, then, are limited in
their type of response to a stimulus. Man, by
comparison, is highly adaptable and can vary
his responses in order to deal with a much
greater variety of stimuli.

Stimuli at Work

If we think of behavior as a bullet being
fired from a gun, stimuli can be compared to
the finger that pulls the trigger. Just as the
finger is needed to move the trigger, so the
stimuli must usually be present to move the
animal to action. A gun must be loaded and
cocked before it will fire. The readiness of an
animal to behave in a particular way—its

17

urge to act — can be compared to this preparing of the gun.

For example, female mammals do not react to a courting male at all times, but only during specific periods when they themselves are ready for mating. At these times, substances from the ovaries and other glands of the body — the hormones — circulate in the blood and stimulate the urge to mate. Experiments have been done with young roosters that had not developed behavior natural to fully mature birds. After being given injections of male hormone the roosters began to attack other young birds and tried to mate with them. The hormone injections had aroused behavior that could otherwise have taken place only when this substance had been naturally produced by the adult bird.

We do not always know the cause of readiness to behave. Sometimes we say that the animal has a *drive* to mate, to find food, or to make a nest. Drives of this kind are dependent upon the presence of hormones in the blood, but there are other conditions that also directly influence behavior. Blood normally contains certain proportions of sugar. When an animal has not eaten food for some time the level of sugar in the blood drops below the normal amount. This affects a part of its brain and makes it seek food.

Above: Experiments show that hormones — glandular substances circulating in the blood — affect not only behavior but also appearance. Upper pictures show a castrated cock before and after injections with male hormone. Lower pictures show a normal cock before and after injections with female hormone.

The internal state of the animal not only produces drives to certain kinds of behavior, but may also change the usual responses to stimuli. A well-fed animal will behave differently from a hungry one, not only toward food — which is to be expected — but also in its reactions to other stimuli. For example, the sheep tick's usual reaction to light is altered completely by hunger. When they are well fed, sheep ticks move away from light. But when hungry they climb to the top of grass blades, away from the darkness of the turf where they usually live, to expose themselves to the sun. A planarian worm changes its behavior toward water currents according to its internal conditions. When its eggs are ripe, the planarian turns upstream against the current, but after depositing its eggs it goes downstream with the current.

This shows us that some behavior is not rigidly fixed, although change is possible only within certain limits. The limits of animal behavior have their advantages; they produce a kind of efficiency that saves time and energy by preventing unsuitable behavior. It would be pointless for an animal that is well fed to go on looking for a meal. What it is that makes one pattern of behavior "switch off," and another set of responses come into play, is not yet known.

Right: An animal's behavior is often influenced strongly by its internal state. During the breeding season the instinctive urge of this reed warbler to thrust food into the open mouths of her nestlings is unaffected by the fact that she is feeding a young cuckoo that she has hatched instead of her own young.

Behavior of many species shows that the bond between a newly born animal and its mother is stronger than any other. The survival of the group, especially in the wild, may depend on the strength of such a bond. Left: The mare (center, on facing page) has driven away her yearling, rejecting him in favor of her young foal.

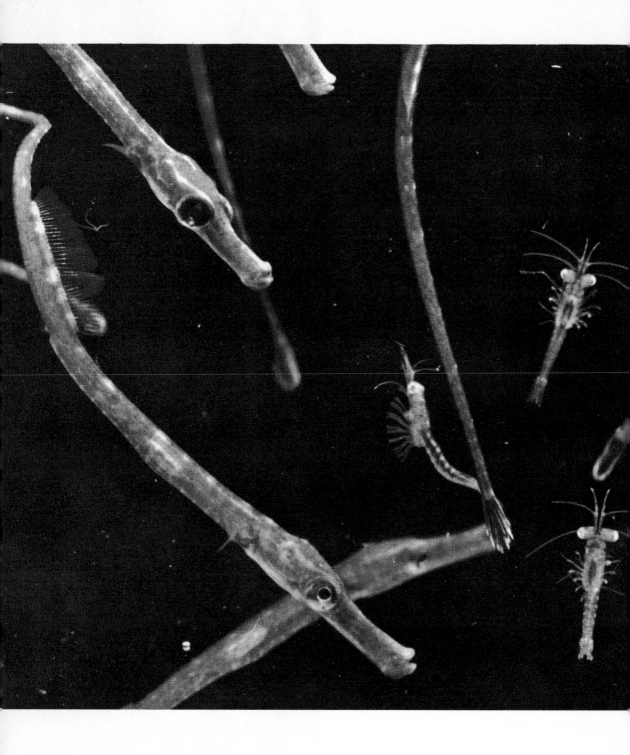

Unlike man, many newborn animals are able to perform a variety of important activities just as efficiently as adult members of their species. These newly hatched pipefish, for instance, are already hunting small shrimps. Their ability not only to hunt but to seek the right food is instinctive.

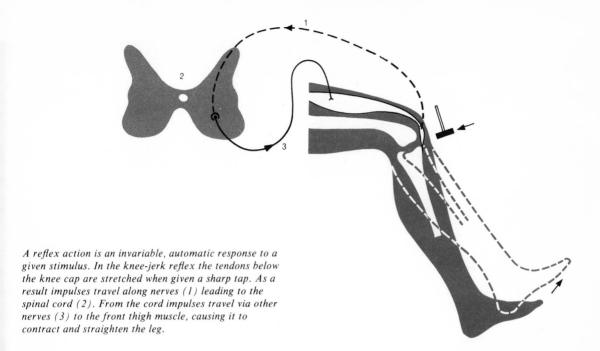

A reflex action is an invariable, automatic response to a given stimulus. In the knee-jerk reflex the tendons below the knee cap are stretched when given a sharp tap. As a result impulses travel along nerves (1) leading to the spinal cord (2). From the cord impulses travel via other nerves (3) to the front thigh muscle, causing it to contract and straighten the leg.

Instinct and Reflex

Much of the behavior of insects and birds changes little, or not at all, to suit new conditions. All the insects or birds within each species follow the same patterns of behavior, for instance, during courtship and mating time. Behavior of this kind is called *instinctive*. We mean by this behavior that is inborn and is neither learned nor modified by experience. It seems as though the animal is brought into the world equipped to behave in ways best suited to certain of its activities. At birth, many animals can not only eat and digest their food but are able to hunt and catch it as efficiently as an adult. When sexually mature most animals know instinctively the often complex rituals of courtship, and can mate and care for their young without having to learn how to do it.

Instinctive behavior is not to be confused with simple actions that arise from reflexes. Reflex actions depend upon the *reflex arc;* that is, sets of nerves that connect the sense organs (which receive the stimuli), through the spinal cord, to the muscle or gland (the effector) that carries out the response. The familiar knee-jerk reflex is an example of how this works in man. By hitting the tendon below the knee cap you stretch the sense organs in the tendon, thus stimulating them. At the blow, impulses travel along the nerve leading to the spinal cord. There connections are made to nerves leading from the cord to the nerve in the large muscle of the upper leg. The impulses cause the leg muscle to contract and to pull the leg straight. All healthy humans have this reflex. The response is both unconscious and automatic. We do not *decide* to make the leg jerk upwards. Instead the impulses causing it to do so do not reach the brain until after the response has been made.

Since many reflexes of this kind are protective it is an advantage for the responses to take place in as short a time as possible. The reflex arc works as a kind of short cut, eliminating the time it would take an impulse to travel to the brain and produce an answering set of impulses leading to action.

Reflexes may seem very like the instinctive drives that were described earlier, but there are important differences. A reflex usually involves only one muscle or a set of muscles, while instinctive patterns concern the whole animal. When a peacock displays its tail many muscles are called into play in order to spread the bird's fan of feathers. Also a reflex will work only so long as the particular sense organ concerned is being stimulated. In contrast, instinctive behavior, once it has been set in action, continues even after the stimulus which first set it in motion has disappeared.

Learning to Behave

However, both instinctive behavior and reflexes are invariable. Given certain stimuli they always occur and each conforms to a fixed pattern. Before an animal can alter its behavior it must be able to draw on its past experience. In other words, it must be able to *learn*. If it is able to learn, the animal may often be able to select from a range of possible ways to solve a problem. If changes occur in its surroundings the animal is then able to alter its behavior to suit the changes, instead of always responding in an identical way to particular stimuli. When an animal learns, it becomes better and better at performing the right action, just as a child does in learning to read or do arithmetic. In many ways the behavior of a child learning lessons and a rat working its way through a maze to find food are much the same. However, there are important differences, and many scientists feel that it is dangerous to apply directly the data from animal experiments to human learning.

The ability to choose different sorts of actions to meet different situations is the kind of learning that can help in a great variety of situations. For example, a child learns to recognize the letters of the alphabet and later is able to read words that may be written, or printed in letters of many different styles. The child can also recognize the letters from what-

Above: This chimpanzee shows intelligence in getting a banana out of the long, open-ended box with the aid of a wooden pole deliberately placed nearby. Unless the history of an animal is known, it is impossible to judge whether such behavior reveals genuine insight or whether the animal is drawing on memories of similar experiences either in captivity or in the wild.

Below: "Generalization of learning" — the ability to use knowledge acquired in answering one problem to solve similar problems — is shown in experiments on this pigeon. The bird was trained to peck a given number of times at the transparent disc when light of a certain color appeared on it. It also pecked at other colors. The number of pecks for each other color was in proportion to its difference in wave length from the original color.

ever angle they are shown, even upside down. This is called the *generalization of learning,* and there are few animals other than man that are capable of it.

It is sometimes difficult to distinguish between learned behavior and intelligent, or insightful, behavior. When we say that an animal shows insight, we imply that it "sees" the answer to a problem directly. It seems to understand the problem and carry out the correct action at once instead of making many attempts and gradually eliminating its errors. But this sort of behavior is not easy to recognize without knowing a great deal about the animal's way of life.

At one time it was thought that chimpanzees showed remarkable intelligence when they used sticks to obtain food placed out of their reach during laboratory experiments. The apes were believed to be finding a solution to a problem that they had never experienced. But further studies of chimpanzees in the wild showed that they often use sticks to knock fruit off trees, and it was realized that their experience in their natural surroundings helped them in solving a similar problem in a different environment.

Stories about what animals do, while they may be interesting and true, are not necessarily helpful to the scientific study of behavior. We need to know, in detail, the specific conditions in which the animals carry out particular activities. At best, the unaided human eye can get only a general impression of behavior. For this reason, moving-picture photography is of great importance because it provides permanent records of animal behavior which can be examined over and over again.

If we are to know precisely *what* an animal is responding to, we must keep rigid control over the stimuli affecting it. Under natural conditions many different stimuli — sight, sound, smell, and light — are all reaching the animal at the same time. An analysis of what touches off a particular response can be done only by bringing the animal into the laboratory and presenting it with one stimulus at a time. Here the brightness and direction of light, for example, can be controlled and all sound cut off so that we can see the response to the one stimulus. But even under these conditions great care has to be taken. An animal usually regards a situation in terms different to those of man. And, even, under the best experimental conditions the animal may respond to something of which humans are totally unaware. But conditions in a laboratory are artificial and cannot exactly duplicate the natural surroundings of the animal. Still, it is only by laboratory analysis that the environment can be taken to pieces, and each part of it tested individually to observe its effect on the animal's behavior.

2. Stimuli and the Senses

An animal is kept informed about its environment and what is going on in it through a variety of sense organs. These organs are equipped to receive stimuli and to pass them to the central nervous system. An animal that lacks an organ sensitive to sound, let us say, would be unable to receive or react to sound stimuli. This would limit the animal's behavior by restricting the number of things in its environment to which it could react. The ability of each type of sense organ to react to stimuli varies greatly between different species. For instance, an animal may be able to distinguish between light and dark. But if the structure of its eyes is too simple to form an image, it will be unable to see shapes or patterns.

An animal relies on its senses – such as sight, smell, hearing, touch for finding food and avoiding enemies. These scallops sense the presence of a starfish through their eyes (the small black dots), by touch (using their slender tentacles), and, possibly, by a sense of smell. The information received through their senses stimulates the scallops to move away from the starfish.

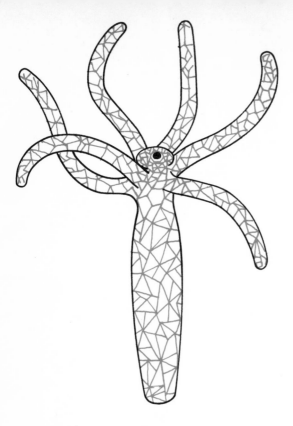

Above: Hydra have a simple network of nerves (red) but no brain. Below: Starfish have a ring of nerves around the mouth and other nerves along each arm. Flatworms have nerves leading from a primitive form of brain called a ganglion. Crickets have additional ganglia at points along the body. Lizards have both a well-developed brain and a spinal cord.

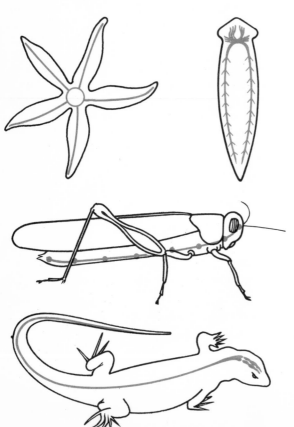

The Work of the Nerves

Most stimuli are forms of energy: radiant energy in the case of light and heat; mechanical energy in sound, touch, and pressure; and chemical energy in the molecules of the substances that are smelled or tasted. But energy in these forms cannot travel along the nerves that run from the sense organs. Only nerve impulses can go by this path to the central nervous system. Stimuli received through the sense organs must therefore be converted into a kind of code, the "code" of the nerve impulses.

When a nerve is active, chemical substances move in and out of the nerve and produce electrical charges. The passage of nerve impulses along nerves has been recorded with very sensitive electrical devices. It has been found that the size of the electrical change for any one nerve is constant: *full strength or not at all*. It is said to obey the "all or nothing" law. This means that weak stimulation is not shown by weak impulses or strong stimulation by strong ones. Instead the strength of the stimulus is measured by frequency—the number of impulses passing through the nerve every second. Thus, low frequency indicates a "weak" stimulation, and high frequency a "strong" one.

Something has to take place in a sense organ to convert the energy of each stimulus into nerve impulses. The process can be compared with that which takes place in a microphone. The sound waves that hit the diaphragm of the microphone cause changes in the electrical circuit. These changes pass along the wire to the loud-speaker where they are reconverted into sound. The mechanical energy of the sound has been transformed into electrical energy that can pass along the wire. When one form of energy is converted into another the process is called *transduction*. We hear a lot about transducers nowadays because they are essential parts of many electronic machines. An example is the photoelectric cell. This acts like an eye and when light falls on the cell its electrical resistance is changed. An electronically controlled door can be made to open when a person walks across—and thereby interrupts—a light beam directed on a photoelectric cell.

Transducers are among man's more recent

inventions, but animals have had built-in transducers in their sense organs since the beginnings of recognizable animal life. The survival of an animal species depends on the efficiency of its responses to the environment. Therefore continuous improvement in the efficiency of the processes that make these responses possible must play a large part in the evolution of all animal life. The ways in which these biological transducers convert stimuli into nerve impulses are not yet known, although scientists are beginning to find out a little about some of them.

Stimuli are represented, then, by impulses that vary in frequency according to their strength. This code is far too simple to explain the complex nature of the stimuli received from an environment containing many different colors, shapes, sounds, smells, and movements. So far we have been discussing what happens in *one* nerve fiber, but every nerve is a bundle of many different fibers. One stimulus may be represented by a high frequency in one fiber and also by a lower frequency in another fiber. In this way the nature of complex stimuli are translated into the code carried by the impulses. This, however, is only part of the story. There is much more to be discovered about how the information, gathered by its sense organs, is carried to the spinal cord and brain.

How the nature of the stimulus—radiant,

The speed of responses to stimuli varies greatly from species to species. A cat's rapid responses, shown in the Egyptian wall painting (right), contrast with those of a jellyfish (above) in which a nerve impulse may take up to one second to pass around the animal's body.

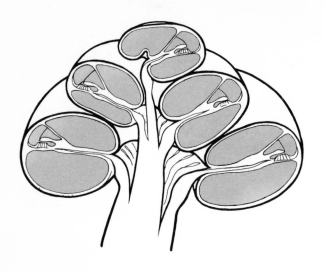

Sense organs operate by converting one form of energy into another. Sound reaches the human inner ear, seen in cross-section (above), in the form of a mechanical stimulus. Sensitive cells, moved by the vibration of the liquid in the inner ear, stimulate the auditory nerve by converting the sound into impulses that are transmitted to the brain. Brain interprets impulses as sound. In the human eye (below) the pigment in cells of retina (blue) changes chemically when light falls on it and stimulates the optic nerve.

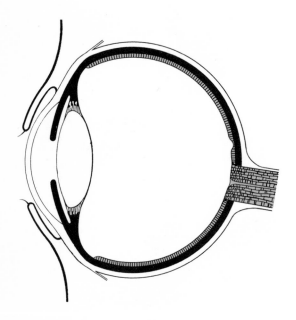

mechanical, or chemical—is determined is yet another problem. As we have seen, the impulses in the nerves are alike in that they all consist of electrical charges. How then are distinctions made between the signals that come from, say, light-sensitive organs and those that come from taste organs? In the brains of mammals there are specific areas of the cortex, or outer layer, of the cerebrum that are concerned with vision, hearing, smell, and so forth. These are the receiving centers (called projection areas) to which coded information from the eyes, ears, nose, and other sense organs is carried.

The brain interprets the impulses arriving at a particular projection area as being the kind that the area normally deals with. For example, if something hits your eye, you may see stars and flashes of light. This is because your brain interprets the impulses reaching the visual area as being caused by light when, in fact, they are the result of a mechanical stimulation—the blow on your eye. The area at which the impulses arrive enables the brain to classify the information carried from the sense organs by the nerves.

An essential part of a sense organ is the cell that acts as a transducer and starts the impulses caused by stimulation. A number of other structures help the transducer by collecting the stimulus. In many mammals, for instance, the trumpet-like outer flap of the ears collects sound. It is then conducted across a chain of bones to the inner ear, where the vibrations pass through a liquid containing sensitive cells and cause them to be stimulated mechanically. In the eyes of animals the transduction is done chemically. The light-sensitive cells at the back of a mammal's eye contain a special *visual pigment* that is changed chemically by light. This chemical change causes impulses to start in the nerve. In darkness, the pigment is restored to its original state, ready for use again.

Sight

In the range of animal life from simple worms to mammals, the sense organs for sight vary from small groupings of sensitive cells to highly complex structures. Sea urchins do not seem to have eyes, as such, but light

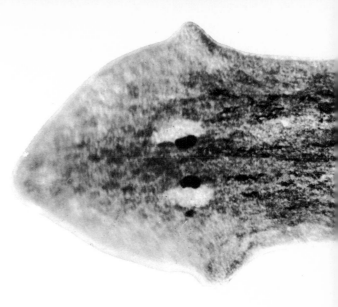

affects them by acting directly on their nerves. The movement of their spines is often the only indication that they have been stimulated by the removal of a source of light. These spines move when they are in shadow. By arranging for a spot of shadow to fall onto a nerve only — and not onto the whole spine — it can be shown that the nerve is performing the function of a sense organ. In other words, the nerve itself acts as a kind of eye.

A group of two or three sensitive cells forms the eye of a flat worm known as a planarian. These cells are almost completely enclosed by a black pigment through which light cannot pass. The eye can thus be used to tell the direction from which the light is coming, for the cell will be fully stimulated only when a small opening in the pigment is pointing straight at the light.

A *lens* represents the next advance in the efficiency of vision. The lens, firstly, serves to focus light rays onto the sensitive cells, thus improving still further their sensitivity to direction. In addition, the lens enables the eye to deal with weaker light by concentrating what little there is onto the cells. Eyes of this kind are found in worms, scallops, and clams, to mention only a few animals.

However, efficient vision depends not only upon the focusing properties of the lens but also upon the structure of the cells in the *retina* that receive the light. Each of these cells receives only a fraction of the image. An image received on a small number of cells will be split up into a number of large dots and will be blurred. If there are many cells the image will consist of many small dots and the details will be clearer.

In order to receive "sharp" images of objects at varying distances, the eye needs to have some way of adjusting the focus of the lens. This is called *accommodation,* and is made possible by special structures in the eyes of vertebrates. Muscles attached to the lens in the eye are able to contract and allow the lens to take a rounded shape. This shortens its focus in order to form clear images of near objects. When the muscles relax, the pressure of the fluid in the eyeball makes the ligaments holding the lens pull on it and flatten it. This lengthens its focus and provides clear images of distant objects.

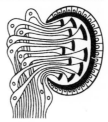

The eye of a planarian (top) is shown in diagram above. The light-sensitive cells are screened by an opaque pigment that admits light from only one direction. Below: The more complex eye of a marine worm has a gelatinous lens that directs light on to the ends of pigmented cells that comprise a simple retina.

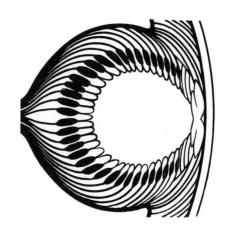

The image that is formed in the eye is curved, but in mammals (including man) this curve does not have the same radius as the curve of the retina. The result is that the image is absolutely sharp only if the object is located at a point along the optical axis of the eye—that is, along an imaginary straight line passing through the centers of both the lens and the eyeball. Objects to either side of the axis may be within the *field of vision,* but their image will be blurred. When we want to look at an object and get a clear image, we move our head and eyes to bring it into position. In birds, the curve of the retina follows the curve of the image. Thus the whole field of vision is in sharp focus. This is one of the factors that give birds such keen sight.

The accommodation muscles of the eye are not the only special organs found in vertebrate vision. In front of the lens there is also an *iris,* a pigmented area through which no light can pass. It also contains muscles. Light travels into the eye through the *pupil,* a hole in the center of the iris. The pupil can be made smaller by contraction of one set of muscles of the iris, or larger by contraction of another set muscles. In fact, the iris acts like the "stop" of a camera in its control of the amount of light that enters the eye. In dim light the pupil is enlarged to admit all the light that is available. In bright light it is smaller. This reaction of the iris muscles to different amounts of light is an example of a reflex.

Not all vertebrates have circular pupils. A cat's eye, for instance, has a vertical slit. It also has a reflective layer behind its retina, so that any light that passes through the cells unabsorbed is reflected back for use. This is why a cat's eyes shine at night—its iris is fully open and light from a flashlight or a car's headlights is reflected from the back of the eye.

An eye that works in air does not necessarily work in water. This is because the way in which a lens focuses light rays depends upon the medium through which the rays pass. If we open our eyes under water, everything is out of focus. This is because the water resting against the *cornea* (or transparent layer) of

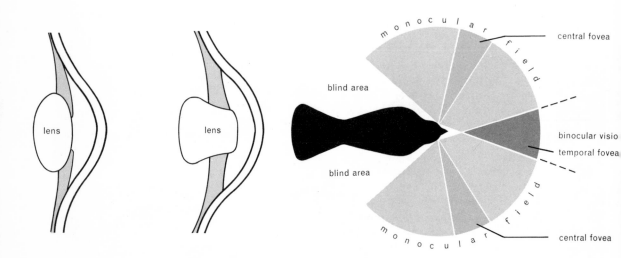

In the eyes of mammals, birds, and reptiles objects at various distances are brought into sharp focus by action of accommodation muscles. Above: In this bird's eye the muscles, shown in blue, are (left) relaxed, allowing the lens to focus on distant objects; and (right) contracted and squeezing the lens to enable it to focus on objects close at hand.

Most birds have monocular vision, since objects in the greater part of their visual field lie within range of only one of their eyes. A few birds, including hawks and eagles, have binocular vision for objects directly in front of them. The diagram above shows a hawk's field of vision. The foveae are small areas of the retina giving very acute daytime vision through the arcs shown.

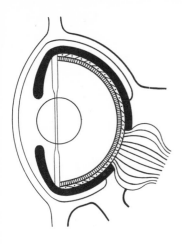

In some marine animals acute underwater vision depends on a spherical lens. An example is the squid's eye (above) which in structure is similar to that of man.

As the engraving below shows, cormorants have long been employed to catch fish for men. Cormorants are used for this purpose because they have acute vision both in air and under water and they can alter the shape of their lenses to suit either medium.

the eyeball transmits light in a different way from air. But if we wear a diving mask that holds air against our eyes, we can see quite clearly. A fish's eye has a lens that is round, like a marble, a shape suited to underwater vision. Some birds, such as the cormorant, have eyes that work in both air and water, for they need to see the fish they are trying to catch when they swim beneath the surface. This is made possible by special muscles that squeeze the lens into a more rounded shape when the birds are submerged.

Retinas of vertebrates are usually made up of two types of cells, *rods* and *cones*. The rod cells are sensitive to feeble light. They are useful at night, but the pigment in them is bleached and loses its sensitivity in bright light. The cones are for daylight vision and, because they are more tightly packed than rods, they give more acute vision. Only the cones are sensitive to color, and the main reason we are not able to distinguish colors at night is that the cones do not react to weak light. Owls and other nocturnal animals owe

their acute night vision to a comparatively large number of rod cells in their retinas.

This type of eye is very well adapted for use by vertebrates. But there is another efficient type—the *compound eye*—found in insects, crabs, lobsters, and some other animals. As its name implies, the compound eye is made up of many smaller "eyes." Each of these cells, called an *ommatidium,* has sensitive cells and a lens of its own. But each ommatidium works like an individual cell of the retina of a vertebrate eye. Each reacts only to what lies directly in front of it and its lens serves only to concentrate the light, not to form an image. Here again, the image is built up of a series of spots. The more ommatidia there are the more numerous are the spots and the sharper the total image. In the eye of a fly or a honey-bee there may be thousands of these ommatidia. Such insects are able to distinguish a number of shapes. An advantage of this type of eye is that it has no difficulty in focusing or accommodating, and works almost as well under water as in air.

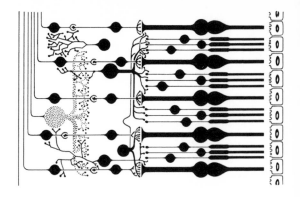

Diagram shows layout of light-sensitive cells in the human retina. Cone and rod cells are at right; the rods are thinner and grouped in threes. Light enters from the left, causing pigment in cone and rod cells to react; the "message" is passed to the optic nerve fibers, leading away at left, which transmit impulses to the brain.

Below: An European owl dives on its prey. Owls and other nocturnal animals owe their keen night vision to the high number of rod cells in the retina.

In some insect eyes the ommatidia are arranged to provide all-round vision. The eyes lie on either side of the head, with ommatidia pointing in directions that describe almost a complete hemisphere. Many vertebrates have somewhat similar all-round vision. Some birds' eyes, for instance, are set wide apart and point sideways, rather than forward, so that each eye covers the area lying on its side.

In general, birds and insects do not have the *binocular* vision typical of monkeys, apes, and man. We are able to use both eyes to look at a single object. Because of this we get a *stereoscopic,* or three-dimensional, image that helps us to judge the distance of the object. A few birds and insects also have binocular vision because what lies directly in front of their heads is just within the field of vision of both eyes. The shrike can accurately spear its prey with its beak because of this, while binocular vision enables the dragonfly larva to judge the precise moment at which to shoot out a special grasping organ, called the mask, it uses to seize its prey.

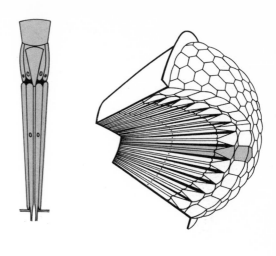

The compound eye (above, right) of insects and some other animals is composed of thousands of smaller "eyes" called ommatidia. Each ommatidium (above, left) has a lens and a crystalline cone that concentrate a narrow band of light, so that the total image on the retina consists of thousands of small dots, rather like a newspaper photograph viewed through a magnifying glass. Below: The compound eyes of a house fly.

Hearing

Just as there are different types of eye, so there are different kinds of hearing organs. One type is found, for example, in vertebrates, the other mainly in insects. Both collect sound waves in much the same way, but the mechanism of hearing is different in each.

Sound waves consist of movements of the molecules of the air. When a sound is made, groups of molecules vibrate. That is, they are pushed together at one moment and apart the next, like shunting freight cars on a railway siding. The *frequency* of a sound is the number of vibrations, that the sound produces in a second.

As the molecules in air alternately push together and spring apart, the air pressure fluctuates. The movement of the molecules either alters the pressure on the outer surface of the eardrum, or it alters the position of the eardrum itself. A mammal's ear works on the first principle, and an insect's on the second. The first depends upon the presence of an eardrum that closes off a sealed cavity. This means that as the pressure changes build up, they make the eardrum bulge out or draw in according to whether the pressure outside the cavity is lower or higher than that inside it.

In the case of the second principle insects have an eardrum with air circulating on both sides. Thus it can move freely by displacement by the molecules of the air. Hairs can also be moved in this way, and some insects pick up air vibrations through movement of hairs on their bodies.

Whichever the principle upon which the ear works, there is great variation in the abilities of different species to detect sounds of different frequencies. Insects generally react to rather low frequencies (about 300 cycles per second). These are fairly low notes to us (middle C on a piano has a frequency of 261 cycles per second). Our hearing range is from about 20 cycles to some 18,000 cycles per second. But bats make and hear sounds of frequencies up to 80,000 cycles per second, and porpoises probably hear sounds up to 120,000 cycles. These frequencies are far higher than those we are able to hear.

Although many animals communicate with each other by the use of sound, their "vocabularies" are very limited compared with the

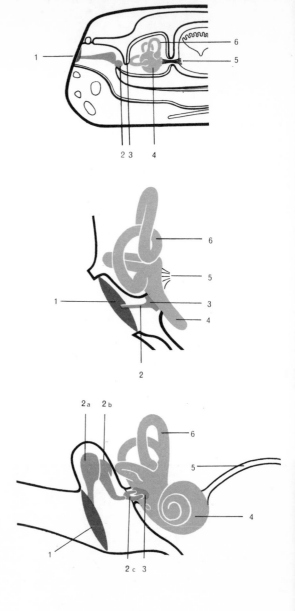

The diagrams above show the main organs that deal with hearing and balance in a frog (top), a pigeon (center), and man (bottom). The colors refer to the outer ear (gray), middle ear (red), and inner ear (blue). Sound waves, producing vibrations in the eardrum (1), move the stirrup bone (2), which in turn causes the oval-window membrane (3) to vibrate. These vibrations stimulate sensitive cells in the fluid-filled cochlea (4), and the auditory nerve (5) transmits their impulses to the brain. In the human ear sound is carried from eardrum to oval window by three bones—the hammer (2a), the anvil (2b), and the stirrup (2c). Vertebrates receive information about balance and movement through the three fluid-filled semicircular canals (6), one for each dimension. Disturbance of the fluid stimulates sensitive hairs lining the end of each canal, indicating the movement of the head in any direction.

human language. Only simple information can be communicated by the noises of most animals. For example, a male bird will sing to let other birds know that he has taken over a territory. Grasshoppers use sound to keep together in the mating season. Fish, too, make noises at mating time. But in all these cases the sounds do little more than establish that the animal is present and in a condition ready to mate.

Animals need to know the direction from which a sound comes. Mammals are able to use their ears to find the loudest direction and thus can place the source. The ears of a cricket are located in the joints of its front legs. As each leg swings forward in turn, the ear scans the surroundings and picks up sounds. By comparing what is received by each ear, the cricket determines the direction of the sound.

Bats and porpoises use their ears for *echolocation* — a highly specialized method of navigating and finding food. As they fly or swim, they emit series of very high frequency squeaks, each lasting for a few thousandths of a second. These sounds are bounced back to them from

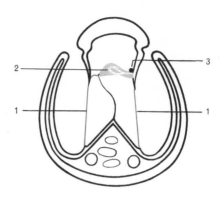

The organs of hearing in the grasshopper (below) are in the front legs. The openings to the organs are visible at the upper end of the tibias. The diagram above shows one such organ in cross-section. The two tympanic membranes (1) correspond to the eardrum in man. Vibrations of the membranes are received by the scolopidia (2), the nearest equivalent to the human cochlea, from which the auditory nerve (3) carries impulses to the central nervous system.

A greater horseshoe bat flying with an insect in its mouth. When flying a bat emits a continuous stream of ultrasonic squeaks, navigating and "homing" on insect prey by echoes received from objects in its path. This method of navigation is similar to sonar.

trees or rocks, insects or fish, as a continuous stream of constantly varying information that tells them which direction to take. The sounds can be heard by the human ear only by first recording them on high-speed tape recorders and then playing them back at lower speeds to reduce their frequency to within our range of hearing.

A bat can tell distance as well as direction by its use of echo-location. The very high frequency of the sounds allows it to judge the position even of very small things. For example, bats flying in a darkened room can avoid wires that are almost as thin as a human hair. Since a bat can catch mosquitoes at the

rate of one about every 30 seconds, its guidance system is very accurate. Tropical, fish-eating bats even use echoes to locate their prey while it is swimming under water.

Lower frequency vibrations, such as the sound of footsteps, are transmitted through the ground, and animals may feel them through their bodies, not through their ears. Changes of pressure on the areas of skin surface in contact with the ground may account for some of this ability, but an insect depends mainly on special sense organs in the legs. Termites use these organs for receiving signals made by other termites, who are thought to indicate alarm by knocking their heads against

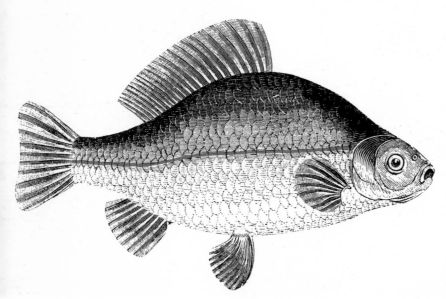

Left: A carp, with its lateral-line system shown in brown. Right: Cross-section of typical lateral-line system. Small openings (1) at the surface of the skin allow water to enter the tubes (2). Movement of water in the tubes (caused, by a neighboring fish) stimulates groups of hairs (3) in sense organs, which send impulses via the lateral line nerve (4) to the central nervous system.

Porpoises also navigate and find food by echo-location. This method enables them to distinguish not only between two fish of almost equal size but also between two objects of identical shape and size made from different materials.

the roof of the "galleries" that they bore in wood.

In water, low frequency vibrations are set up by the movements of anything that wriggles. Fish are very sensitive to vibrations carried in water. The water movement is picked up by the *lateral line system* that runs along each side of a fish's body and over its head. This is a collection of tubes just below the surface of the skin. At intervals along the tubes are small openings to the skin surface. In the tubes groups of hairs are enclosed in a jelly-like substance. When the hairs are bent by the movement of the water in the tubes, impulses travel to the central nervous system.

Fish use this system to locate their prey, for water vibrations caused by other fish will reach the sense organs in one part of the system before another, depending upon the position of the prey. The sense organs also react to water being deliberately pushed against one fish by another as in the courtship behavior of swordtails and other species.

Scent

To man, sight and sound are the most important sources of stimuli from the environment. But for many other animals, and particularly in insects and mammals other than

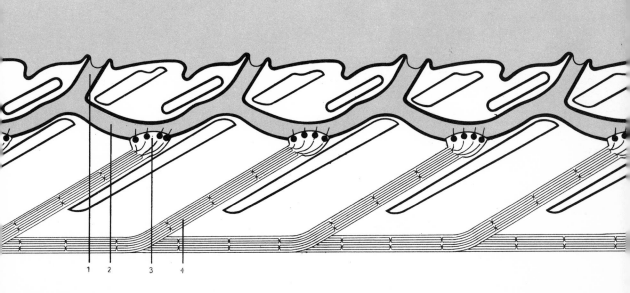

Man, monkeys, apes, and most birds, have a very poor sense of smell compared with most insects and many other vertebrates. The diagrams above show the rear section of the human nasal cavity (top) and its larger, more complex, and much more sensitive counterpart in a deer.

man, this is not so. Dogs, cats, antelope, and most mammals, depend upon their noses to a much greater extent than does man. They are more sensitive to smells than we are, and the scent of their surroundings conveys more to them than it does to us. Mates, enemies, and prey alike are recognized by their scent.

Mammals' noses are similar to those of man. Air is drawn through the nostrils so that chemicals in the atmosphere come into contact with the sensitive cells arranged in a patch on one of the air passages. Insects do not breathe in this way, yet to them scent is as important as it is to the mammals. Insects receive scents through hairs on their antennae, which they twitch about in the air. The hair cells are extremely sensitive; it has been calculated that the scent emitted by only a million molecules (an unimaginably small amount) of certain substances is enough to stimulate them.

Taste

Man uses taste mainly for deciding whether food is palatable or not. This, probably, is also the main use to which all fish, frogs, lizards, and mammals put this sense. Birds, in contrast, seem to have little sense of taste or

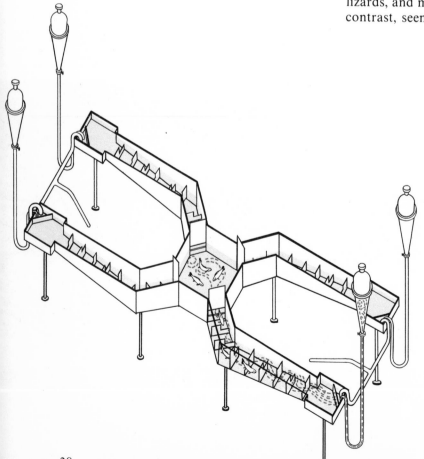

This device is used to test the reaction of young Atlantic salmon to various odors. Water containing different odors (red) flows down the runways toward fish in the central compartment, and the salmon's attraction to, or reaction against, each odor is recorded. These and other tests suggest that the mature salmon's ability to return to its place of birth for spawning may depend on its sense of smell. Possibly the salmon recognizes a specific odor from its home river.

smell, and for most information depend upon their eyes and ears.

It is probably better to refer to taste as the *contact chemical sense,* one reason being that insects have no tongues and their sense of taste is located in their legs. The blowfly and butterfly both have hairs on their feet that are sensitive to contact with chemicals. Though not located in the mouth, these hairs are concerned also with feeding since they are able to detect the amount of sugar in nectar. There are, in addition, similar hairs on the mouth parts which these insects use when collecting their food.

The human tongue seems to be able to distinguish four main tastes—acid, salt, sweet, and bitter—each of which is sensed by a particular area on the tongue's surface. At one time it was believed that many different animals, including insects, had these four tastes. But it seems apparent now that the taste senses of different animals respond in different ways. Frogs, for instance, can taste water. Many of the chemicals that stimulate insects cannot be grouped under the four basic categories of human tastes. It is also difficult to be certain that the great variety of tastes that humans like or dislike can always be explained simply as mixtures of these four categories.

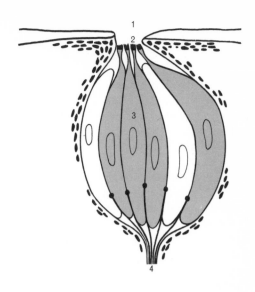

A human tongue (below) can distinguish four basic tastes. Acid is sensed along the sides of the tongue, salt and sweet along sides and front, bitter at the back. Each taste bud (above), located just beneath the surface of the tongue, is sensitive to only one taste. Food mixed with saliva enters the bud through a pore (1) and comes into contact with hair-like sensory organs (2). Each process is connected with a sensory cell (3) that changes chemical reactions to nerve impulses and transmits them via nerve (4) to the brain.

Touch

In most animals the organs dealing with the sense of touch are simple in comparison with those of the eye or ear. They lie embedded in the skin. Each is small—barely visible to the eye in humans—and consists of a nerve ending enveloped by layers of tissue, rather like the leaves of an onion. When pressed, the layers are moved and this stimulates the nerve to send out impulses to the central nervous system. Man and other mammals are capable of distinguishing between many different kinds of sensations through the skin. The senses of touch, pressure, heat, cold, and pain, for instance, are each received by separate groups of nerve cells. In the case of pain, nerve impulses may produce a reflex action.

The hairs of insects, so useful for chemical sensitivity, are often used for touch sense. When an insect brushes against something, hairs on its body are bent over and thus stimulated. The hairs on a blowfly's leg, for instance, will react not only to sugars, acids, and water but also to being pressed.

As we have seen, an ability to sense heat is important for parasites for their life may depend upon the food they get from a warm-blooded animal host and upon the protection they gain by being tucked away among the host's hair or feathers. One of the blood-sucking bugs has pits lined with sensitive hairs on its antennae. In laboratory experiments it has been found that the bug can use this device to find its way to a test tube filled with water that has been warmed to human body temperature.

Pit vipers including rattlesnakes have sense organs that, as far as we know, are unique. They are in pits on the snake's head and enable the animal to detect a warm body only a few feet away. Apparently these pits are sensitive to infra-red rays, invisible to the human eye, that are given out by anything warm. Mammals, being warm-blooded, emit these rays and in this manner the snakes can find the mice and other animals they eat.

Very few animals are able to sense electric fields (although at one time it was thought that migratory birds used the earth's magnetism to navigate). But certain fish in some of the large muddy river estuaries of South America and Africa can form an electric field

The beadlet anemone, a marine animal, (above) depends on tactile sense cells for catching food. A sand eel, trapped by the retreating tide, brushes against the anemone's tentacles, which enclose it and sting it to death.

The star-nosed mole (below) navigates through damp soils with the help of twenty-two highly sensitive, tentacle-like structures on its snout.

around themselves. The electric field alters when another creature swims into it or when the fish approaches underwater obstacles. Thus, by means of this sense the fish can navigate and find food in rivers where the water is too muddy for eyes to be of much use.

Behavior and the Brain

All the sense organs for sight, hearing, smell, taste, and touch pass their information into the brain. Impulses then pass out of the brain and cause the effector system to produce the response to the stimulus just as in the simpler reflex arc described earlier. How this is brought about, and what exactly goes on in the brain, are still largely unknown. Behavior studies help us very little in solving these problems. When we watch an animal, we can see and record the sights, sounds, and smells to which we believe it responds, and we can observe its behavior in detail. But we cannot be certain how the information passed on by the sense organs is decoded or translated in the brain. In other words, observations of behavior alone cannot give us direct information about the nerve impulses that enter the brain. Nor can they tell us how the brain responds to these impulses.

One of the problems still to be solved is whether or not an animal really reacts to a particular stimulus. In tests on an eye removed from an animal it can be shown that two different colors produce two different impulses in the organ's nerve cells. In other words the eye reacts differently to the two colors.

But, the question is does the brain distinguish the differences between them? If the animal's behavior is different in response to each color, we assume that its brain is interpreting, or *perceiving,* the information that reaches it. Perception, or understanding, takes place, if at all, in the brain. And it is the brain that must be able to distinguish between different signals from the sense organs before that which is received can be perceived. We must therefore be cautious in making judgments about the results of tests on isolated sense organs. The fact that the eye responds differently to different colors is no proof that the behavior of the animal as a whole is being influenced by such responses.

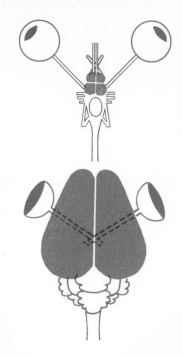

Above: Eye-and-brain diagrams of a codfish (upper) and domestic cat (lower) illustrate the fact that an animal's ability to "understand" depends on its brain size. The eyes of the cod and cat are comparable in size and structure. Although the cat does not necessarily "see" more, it can understand more because the area of its brain that interprets visual stimuli is larger and more complex.

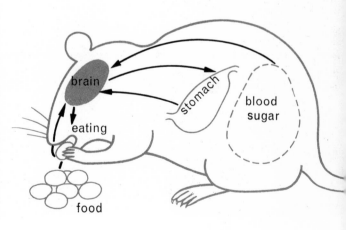

An animal responds not only to external stimuli but also to automatic mechanisms within the body. The diagram shows one such mechanism. The rat's supply of blood sugar is low, and areas of the brain affected by blood-sugar levels are stimulated. As a result nervous impulses pass from brain to stomach, which in turn feeds back hunger pangs to the brain. Other mechanisms indicate to the rat when it has eaten enough.

Termites, which often live in huge mounds like this one in Kenya, have a social organization based on castes. One caste includes the kings and queens, which reproduce the species and sometimes migrate to found new colonies. The sterile castes include soldiers that defend the colony, and workers that build the mound and supply the colony with food.

3. Living in a Society

A human society is, essentially, a group of people living together who share a language and a system of rules and customs that defines their obligations toward one another. This is, of course, an oversimplification. For instance, each individual is also a member of a family — the basic unit of social organization. Each adult works to support himself and, often, his family as well. In a primitive society most adult men grow or catch their own food, make their own tools, and build their own shelters. As societies grow in complexity, however, work ceases to be generalized and becomes divided up into a growing variety of specialized functions — food growing, building, religion, defense, medicine, and so on — which are beyond the scope of any one man.

The nature of each society is defined by the system of techniques and tools that men develop to change nature and make it habitable. These techniques and tools make up a body of social knowledge that is developed and handed on from one generation to the next by word of mouth or by written record. In human societies, this social knowledge, which governs the ways in which individuals and groups behave, is a conscious, man-made phenomenon. In animal societies, however, social behavior is determined by hereditary factors, although many animals are able to modify their patterns of behavior by a limited kind of learning. Owing to the absence of elaborate means of communications between individuals, these patterns are much simpler and more rigid than in a human society.

Specialization for particular work is not a monopoly of human societies. Indeed, it is most fully developed in some insect societies. As a result, these societies have a permanence rather like our own, although they are based very largely upon instinctive behavior. No other social animals have developed a similar division of labor. Each bird in a flock, each antelope in a troop, each fish in a school, is capable of finding its own food and capable of carrying on all the processes of life without aid from its fellows. Whereas under natural conditions an ant cannot live alone away from its colony, a member of one of the higher animal societies can and often does. Some howler monkeys are always excluded from the group, yet are well able to fend for themselves.

Animals that come together to form groups, whether of a few or very many individuals, may remain together only for the breeding season, or only for the remainder of the year. The annual gatherings of millions of Alaskan fur seals in the Pribilof Islands (south of Bering Straits) are a striking example of the way animals collect together only for breeding. During the rest of the year the adult seals are dispersed all over the North Pacific Ocean and along the western seaboard of Canada and the United States.

Many birds live in mixed flocks of males and females during the winter but, as spring approaches, the males leave to establish individual territories to which they attract a mate. So during the breeding season the birds live as breeding pairs and keep other birds out

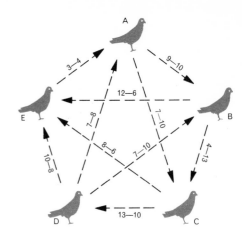

Left: Peck order among chickens rarely changes. In this group (A) — most dominant — has driven (E) — least dominant — into a corner, while (B) prevents (C) and (D) from feeding by pecks. Above: This diagram, based on a series of tests, shows that dominance order is less rigid among a group of female pigeons. In dominance encounters pigeon (A), pecked (B) ten times but lost on nine other occasions. None of the five birds gained absolute dominance over all others, nor dominated any other bird at every encounter.

of their territories. This breaks up the flock until the autumn, when it re-forms. Although a group of animals may stay together from year to year, its organization may alter according to the season. In the mating season a herd of deer will naturally consist of males, each with his group of females. But at other times of the year the males form herds of their own, while the females and their young ones remain together.

How can we decide whether a group of animals is a society or merely a collection of individuals that happen to live in the same area? Like humans, animals can form a society only if they can (and do) communicate with each other. Communication in this sense may include not only sound but also scent, and other types of stimuli. Each animal responds to another's presence. If one is aggressive the other is aggressive or submissive as the case may be—the response is never neutral. The mark that distinguishes a society is the interplay of stimuli and responses that creates a state of interdependence among its members.

Dominance and Leadership

An animal society is usually orderly, with its members arranged in *ranks*. The most aggressive animal is the highest in rank, a position gained by its pugnacity toward the others. He or she *dominates* the rest. The highest in rank has the right to nip or peck any of the *subordinate* animals, and they do not fight back.

Dominance in this form often applies only to one aspect of social life. The animal who is, for instance, dominant for choice of food is not necessarily also dominant in the choice of a mate.

The remaining animals in a society are arranged in a series of decreasing dominance. The second in rank cannot attack the highest rank but can attack all the others and so on down the line to the lowliest animals, who may go short of food and be denied a mate. The effects of social dominance can most easily be observed in the "peck order" of hens in a chicken yard.

The simple series of ranks may be upset by other relationships. For example, a female monkey takes the male's rank when she is paired with him and their young will take the mother's rank. If an animal becomes ill it will almost certainly drop several places in rank. On the other hand, if it is a male and is given an injection of male hormone in a laboratory, it will become more aggressive and may rise in rank. The individual encounters that determine dominance are not really fights for they seldom involve bloodshed. They are more like symbolic trials of strength.

Non-social Groups

Some groups of animals are merely collections of individuals that are reacting to the same environment. Since all the animals are seeking the same kind of living conditions, they tend to crowd into places where those conditions are available. They may be compared with a group of people who huddle together in the doorway of a store to avoid the rain. Wood lice that gather together under the bark of old logs are non-social animals that happen to share an environment. Similarly brittle stars, the slender-armed relatives of the common starfish, will cling to each other if they are in an aquarium tank with nothing else in it. But if glass rods are placed in the tank the animals will clamp on to them instead of twining themselves around each other. In both cases the brittle stars are getting the maximum of touch stimulation by contact with each other or with the rods. A similar kind of touch stimulation is obtained by the wood lice when they congregate under the bark. These are not examples of social behavior, however, because the animals' reactions are not mutual but one-sided.

Such non-social groups seem to help the animals to survive, for individuals grouped together in this way seem to live longer than ones that are isolated. Why this should be is not at all clear, but the effect of numbers on survival has been observed in many species. One ant alone, for instance, is less likely to survive than an ant that is one of a pair. Two ants are more vulnerable than individuals that are in groups of three, and so on. Natural selection, then, favors the group rather than

Wood lice, non-social animals that happen to share a habitat, are stimulated by contact with each other. As individuals in such a group tend to live longer than isolated wood lice, such non-social gatherings may mark a stage in the evolutionary development of an animal society.

Social animals often act cooperatively for mutual protection against predators. Starlings normally fly in open formation (above, left). But on sighting a hawk, they close ranks (right) so that in diving on one of them the hawk would risk injury by colliding with the rest.

Musk ox herds (below) gather into a tight defensive group when threatened by wolves, their only natural enemy. This reaction to danger has made them a much easier target for the guns of hunters who value their fur and meat.

the individual, and it is likely that gatherings of individuals mark an evolutionary stage in the development of an animal society.

Advantages of Social Living

One of the main reasons why animals live in flocks, herds, schools, and so on, is that there is safety in numbers. For instance, a hawk will dive on a solitary starling but will not attack a flock of starlings for the good reason that it might injure its wings when plummeting down among them. When a goldfish feeds on water fleas (Daphnia) it will eat fewer of them if the fleas are in a densely packed swarm than if they are widely scattered. Possibly the fish is confused by the concentration of animals. Completely different species sometimes offer mutual protection, as in the case of the mixed troops of baboon and impala antelope in the East African grasslands. A warning cry from either a baboon or an impala when it senses danger is enough

to put both apes and antelopes to flight. Moreover, cheetahs that would attack if the impala were alone are chased off by the baboons. These three examples provide evidence of the protection given by living in a group, in spite of the fact that large numbers of animals are very conspicuous to an enemy.

Group life has other advantages, especially in the effects of mutual stimulation upon individuals. Like most humans, animals living in groups tend to mature earlier than solitary animals of the same species. The animals also seem to imitate each other. If one of them is feeding it stimulates the others to feed. This kind of effect is called *social facilitation* and is a powerful force among social animals. For example, a chick that has just finished feeding will start to eat once more if it is placed with a group of hungry chicks that have just begun to eat. Similarly, but in reverse, a hungry chick will not eat immediately if set down at some food among chicks that have already taken all they can and have stopped eating. Similar effects on appetite can sometimes be seen among small children at parties.

Social Behavior

Every group of social animals exhibits various patterns of behavior—sometimes simple, sometimes very complex—that help to bind the individual to his society. Groups of apes and monkeys often consist of enlarged families that include a number of near relations. Howler monkeys make their way, branch by branch, through the forest in bands that are usually composed of three males, eight females, three infants still dependent upon their parents, and four older but still immature monkeys. As "hangers-on," but not as members of the group, a number of solitary males follow. In spite of their smaller numbers, it is the males who lead the group, who defend it, and who control its dominance structure.

Baboons of the African plains, on the other hand, move at ground level in larger troops, often of 80 or so individuals. These are subdivided into groups of individual males with "harems" of several females. The subdivisions change frequently. A female may change her male partner several times during her lifetime. They are extremely reluctant to move

Gorillas live in small family groups that include a number of closely related adults and young. Essentially nomadic, gorillas often build temporary shelters in trees to sleep in at night.

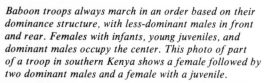

Baboon troops always march in an order based on their dominance structure, with less-dominant males in front and rear. Females with infants, young juveniles, and dominant males occupy the center. This photo of part of a troop in southern Kenya shows a female followed by two dominant males and a female with a juvenile.

Below, baboons and impala antelope often live together for mutual defense. The baboons' acute vision and the impalas' keen sense of smell make it almost impossible for a predator to approach unnoticed.

The cohesion and stability of the baboon troop depend not simply on the urge to mate but on a wide range of social behavior. Grooming, for instance, is one of the most important activities that help to bind baboons into groups. Grooming not only removes parasites and dirt but also seems to give pleasure to the recipient. Below a baboon suckling her infant is groomed by another adult female, who will later be groomed in return. Juveniles and adults spend several hours a day grooming each other.

about in darkness, and at night the troop takes to the trees to sleep in safety.

Baboons continually groom each other. The females are especially busy because they groom the infants as well as other females and the males. A baboon will go up to another and beg to be groomed by standing with the back of its neck toward its companion. The groomer will go carefully through the first one's hair, picking out dirt and parasites. The animal being groomed relaxes and seems to go into a trance, for it closes its eyes and sinks back on its haunches. Other species of monkey will do this as well, and grooming pairs are a common sight in zoos. This is true social behavior in that it is mutual. After a time the roles are reversed, the groomer becoming the groomed.

The most dominant males are groomed more often than the others. Indeed, this appears to be one of the rewards of being dominant. They also take the best feeding and sitting places. There is no fight if they find their place occupied, for the other male recognizes that he is subordinate and surrenders his position without argument. One of the signs of a dominant baboon is its raised tail. This may be a sort of badge that the other baboons accept as showing that its wearer is privileged.

The dominant males are not the leaders of the baboon troop. When the troop moves around its territory (usually an area of between three and six square miles), it is led by the less dominant males, followed by females and juveniles, then females with infants and the dominant males. Other, less dominant males bring up the rear. Leadership of a group by its less aggressive members is a factor common to many species of animal.

It is likely that grooming is of greater importance than any other influence in keeping the group together. It has often been thought that the urge to mate was the factor that kept apes and monkeys in groups. But among the baboons a mature female is in *estrus,* or in heat, only for one week in the month. When she is pregnant or nursing an infant she cannot come into estrus. Consequently there may be long periods in the life of the baboon group when none of the females is ready to mate. Yet the group stays together. This suggests strongly that other factors are more important than sexual ones with these particular baboons, although this may not apply to other apes and monkeys.

There is no question of sexual bonds holding social insect groups together. Mutual stimulation, sometimes in the form of grooming, but more particularly through the giving and receiving of food, is the most important factor holding insect societies together.

Reproduction is obviously a motive for the formation of summer herds of red deer, a European species. In these the males fight for dominance and for mates. Unlike the long-established and more slowly changing patterns of dominance in a primate group, those in a red-deer herd have to be re-established each September and last only for the short mating period. For the dominance of a male applies here only to his ability to collect hinds, or females, around him for mating.

This becomes apparent if the herd is disturbed. Immediately the hind that leads the hind herd in the out-of-breeding season re-asserts her leadership and the rest follow after her. The stags, now reduced in importance, tag along behind. When they are not mating, the stags forming an all-male herd appear not to have dominance relationships, and their herd is more loosely knit than that of the hinds. The hinds have young with them that, when about three years old, will leave to join the stags if they are males.

Meanwhile, the herd composed of mothers and offspring, is a more closely knit group than the stag herd. Possibly leadership develops along lines similar to that in a flock of sheep. A ewe follows its mother even after she has had a lamb herself. In turn, the lamb's female offspring will follow her. The sheep flock is held together by the mother-child relationship. The rams keep away from the flock.

The social organization of apes, monkeys, deer, and sheep—all of which are nomadic animals—makes an interesting comparison with that of other animals, such as prairie dogs, which settle in one place. These rodents live in the western states. They make burrows forming "townships" that may spread over several acres. A burrow has more than one opening, around each of which is a pile of earth dug out by the animals. This mound prevents flood water from entering the burrow and drowning the inhabitants. It is also a grandstand from which the prairie dog can look around and from which he signals danger and ownership. The inhabitants of the towns are divided into neighborhood groups, averaging one male, three females, and six offspring. This group knows the boundaries of the territory that it owns within the township. Each member has an elaborate "set of maners" for meeting and challenging the dogs he may find on his group's territory. He approaches the intruder with open mouth and bared teeth. If the other animal does the same and they "kiss," all is well—a friend has been recognized and the animals may groom each other. One rolls on to its back, presenting its underside to the other. Here again grooming between members of the group serves to keep them together, but its effect is reinforced by the aggressive attitude shown toward strangers. Probably the grooming after an encounter decreases the aggressiveness of the threatening animal.

For most of the year mature males and females of European red deer have little or no contact with each other. Hinds, or females, (below, left) live in herds including immature stags up to three years of age. The mature stags live in smaller, less coherent herds of their own. In the mating season beginning in September the stag herds break up. The stags pursue hind herds and each stag takes possession of as large a group of hinds as he can maintain against the claims of his rivals. Silent at other times, the stag finds voice in the mating season, roaring constantly in order to frighten rivals away from his hinds. His strongest and most determined rivals, however, may be deterred only by defeat in trials of strength (below).

In the wild, many different species usually live harmoniously together if one does not feed upon another. The hippopotamuses above are content to share their section of Congo River bank with pelicans and cormorants. The two bird colonies, although of distantly related species and living on a similar fish diet, do not fight each other and cannot interbreed. Their members show rivalry only toward others of their own kind.

Flamingos commonly establish colonies in which several nests may be crowded into every square yard. Very large colonies such as this one in east Africa, have many thousands of members.

Living in the township offers protection against predators, for at least one prairie dog is always on the lookout for danger. But the structure of the town has other advantages for the inhabitants. The spacing of the territories spreads the animals out over the available grassland and prevents them from exhausting their food stocks. At the same time the grass is kept short enough to deny cover to predators.

In contrast to the prairie dogs, few birds live continuously in flocks. Most join flocks for part of the year. Some, including most birds of prey, are always solitary except when mating and rearing their young. Flocks can contain great numbers of birds. The large gatherings of migratory birds, such as swallows, are just the beginning of the massing together of many of these gatherings to form huge flocks that will follow the migratory route to the winter home.

Often the birds have markings that attract other birds of the same species to join them. Ducks, for example, have vividly colored eye-like patterns on their wings that show when they spread their wings and fly. Ducks can usually recognize the pattern of their own species. They will often follow a duck of their own kind when it flies overhead, displaying its distinctive feather patterns. Mixed flocks of ducks also occur, possibly because the wing patterns of two similar species cannot be distinguished by the birds. Similar special patterns are also found on the tail feathers of various species of wading birds.

Birds may also search for, or be attracted to, a flock by special flocking calls. Some birds separated from the flock will make frequent flocking calls as they hop through the bushes. Then they may stop to listen for answering calls from the flock.

Once in a flock, a bird makes others keep their distance when they are feeding or roosting. If others approach to within what is called its *individual distance* the bird threatens them. In this way the members of a flock are kept well spaced out, with each bird protecting the territory around itself. Individual distance can be observed in the regular spacing of gulls lined up on the edge of a dock or in other birds perched on power lines.

As a flock takes off, turns and wheels in the air, and lands again, it often seems as if

Individual distance is apparent in the swallows perched upon these overhead wires. Attempts by other swallows to overcrowd are met with threats. Although differing in extent between species, individual distance is common to many flocking birds and, probably, to many fish as well.

Gulls (left) and pigeons (right) gather quickly when food is thrown to them. Others nearby are attracted by the cries of the feeding birds. How is it that many birds out of earshot are also attracted? Flocking birds constantly observe the behavior of other birds in the flock. It is likely that birds making for food betray their intention by small but specific details of movement that escape our notice, but are observed and understood even by distant members of the flock.

the birds are no longer individuals but simply parts of a great machine. There is, however, no evidence of a sort of "flock mind" taking control on these occasions. More likely, birds are very sensitive to the behavior of their companions. If one gets ready to fly and stretches its wings in the *flight-intention* movements, the rest take the tip, and the flock rises in a mass. This is another example of social facilitation and shows how readily birds react to stimuli from others of their species. This extends also to feeding, so that if food is found by one member the others know about it at once, and are stimulated to feed by the sight of the bird picking up the food.

The flock may act together to mob a predator, flying down at it, beating it with their wings, and attempting to frighten it off. Many song birds, for instance, will band together with other species to attack owls oʀ cats. Their recognition of owls is very accurate. They will not attack models unless they are owl-shaped and have dark, dappled coloring. A light-colored but otherwise exact model of a little owl will not cause them to mob it. And a barn owl, which is light colored, is not mobbed by song birds on the rare occasions when it flies during the day.

When different species join together for protection against a predator, the same alarm call will serve to arouse each species to the danger. When the European chaffinch gives its characteristic alarm call, all chaffinches and other birds in earshot take cover. It is almost as if a man could give a call that would mean the same thing to apes and monkeys as well as to other men.

It might be thought that the bird that gives the warning would betray its position at the same time. In fact, the call is usually given from behind cover. The sound is pitched in such a way that, for various physiological reasons, it seems likely that the predator would find it very difficult to locate the exact source of the call. Alarm calls are also given by prairie dogs to warn the whole township. The white tails of rabbits and a number of antelope are visual signals that warn others of danger. As the alarmed animals run away, their tails bob about conspicuously and are seen by others.

Just as a flock of birds wheels and turns together so, too, does a school of fish. It is startling to see a school of herring suddenly change direction. The fish are swimming along in a certain direction at one moment. Then, within a fraction of a second, they will all turn at a sharp angle to left or right, keeping in perfect formation. Apart from protection, the main advantages of being a member of a school lies in the facilitation of feeding and reproduction. Black Sea anchovy, for example, form dense schools that may move around in circles when a horse mackerel or other predator is near. The mackerel will be unable to catch any of the fish so long as they stay in their school. Like a hawk after starlings, it can catch only solitary animals or stragglers.

Although schools are formed of fish of both sexes, reproduction does not seem to be the primary purpose. Fish stay in a school because they *see* their companions. A blinded fish will not school. A fish with one blind eye will line itself up with the school on its seeing side. Two fish like this will not swim together if their blinded sides are toward each other but they will if the good eye of each faces the other.

The attraction of fish separated by glass from others shows that the scent of the fish is relatively unimportant in many species. A

Right: The diagrams show four stages in an experiment on schooling behavior among young acara, a small tropical fish. (1) The group schools in a combination of incandescent and fluorescent light. (2) When the fluorescent light is removed the school disperses within a few seconds. (3) When the fluorescent light is restored the acara begin to group together at once and, within a minute or two (4), the school has re-formed.

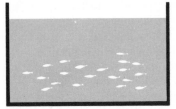

Below: Wooden models of owls used to test the mobbing response of chaffinches. Mobbing seems to be triggered by recognition of general shape and color rather than of specific details such as plumage markings.

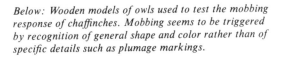

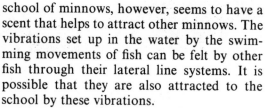

Above: Schooling behavior of silverside fry. Newly
hatched (top) they show little response to each other's
presence. Within a few days (center) they begin to
approach, and line up with, others in their group. After
four weeks (bottom) they swim together as a school.
Right: River trout resting in ranks. The apparent pairing
in each rank may be related to individual distance.

school of minnows, however, seems to have a
scent that helps to attract other minnows. The
vibrations set up in the water by the swimming movements of fish can be felt by other
fish through their lateral line systems. It is
possible that they are also attracted to the
school by these vibrations.

Aggressive behavior like that in a bird flock
does not seem to occur among schooling fish,
although the even spacing of fish in a school
implies the preservation of an individual distance. Perhaps the preferred distance is determined by the intensity of the vibrations set
up by the movements of swimming. However,
when a school is threatened by the approach
of a predator, the ranks close up. Thus the
individual distance—if it can be called this—
of such fish is variable.

The development of schooling among
young herring has been studied. Immediately
after hatching, when they are no more than
five to seven millimeters (about a quarter
of an inch) in length, they dart away if approached by other young. Then, as they grow,
they pass through a stage when an approach
to another from the rear is followed by a short
swim together, while a head-on meeting
causes both fish to swim rapidly away from
each other. Gradually encounters in which
one fish comes to the tail of another become

more frequent. When they are about 10 millimeters (just under half an inch) in length,
both fish waggle the whole of their bodies
when they meet, and will then swim off together. The size of the school develops and
its orderliness increases until, when the fish
are some 15 millimeters long, they form a
miniature school.

If a school is attacked, the fish may scatter
in alarm as soon as a fish is seized. The break-
up of the group is caused by a chemical substance that is released from a fish's skin when
it is injured and acts as an alarm signal. The
chemical spreads quickly in the water. As soon
as another fish senses it, it swims rapidly away.
Fish of other species are also alarmed in some
measure by the substance. Thus, the chemical
may be compared with the general alarm call
of the chaffinch. Not all fish secrete this
chemical in their skin, and it affects only those
species that do secrete it. Members of the
salmon and perch families do not make or
react to it; minnows, carp, and similar species
react most strongly to it.

Fish are kept in schools in ways that are
similar to those by which insects are kept in
their groups. Probably some of the greatest
of insect gatherings are the swarms of locusts
that plague Africa and the Middle East. The
millions of insects in these flying swarms are

carried by the wind and appear as if they are rolling forward over the countryside. Those at the front are continually landing. Then, when they have eaten, they join the rear of the swarm, which has meanwhile passed overhead. Photographs taken with the camera pointed vertically upward through the middle of a swarm will often show many individuals flying away from the general direction followed by the main body. When these individuals come to the edge of the swarm, they turn back toward the center again because they are stimulated by the sight of their companions.

Most people have seen swarms of whirligig beetles skating around on the calm surface of ponds or rivers. The beetles detect movement in the water through their antennae, which they dip in the surface film. It is likely that the whirling swarm of beetles sets up particular kinds of vibrations in the film, so that if an individual strays from the swarm it can find its way back by turning toward the direction from which the vibrations are coming. Possibly scent also helps to keep the swarm together, for these beetles produce a strong smell, rather like that of malt, when they are picked up. Vibrations also help the beetles to find food, for they show the location of small insects that become trapped in the surface film.

Below: A flying locust swarm remains together as a close unit for long periods, but individual locusts constantly change position and flight direction within the swarm. The arrows in the diagram below show the directions in which individual locusts were heading in a three-square-mile swarm flying over south-east Kenya. Many individuals were flying at an angle to the general downwind direction of the swarm, represented by the central line, with the leading edge at the bottom and trailing edge at the top. Note that many locusts near the leading and trailing edges had turned back toward the center of the swarm.

direction of swarm

57

Insect Societies

The most highly organized insect species are the ants, bees, and wasps, and also the distantly related termites, or white ants. These insects live in societies far more elaborate than any other in the animal kingdom apart from those of man. The basis of the social life of ants, for example, is that of a family centered on a reproducing, egg-laying mother with whom the daughters remain as workers. A single fertilized queen ant can found a whole colony—the male dies after mating. The queen will have no workers until the larvae that hatch from her first eggs have developed through the pupal stage and have emerged as adult daughters. They in turn help to feed her, care for the eggs she lays, feed the larvae, open the pupae, and carry out all the other jobs to be done in the colony. The whole colony, in fact, operates as an efficient reproductive machine.

What are the bonds that hold these insect societies together? Certainly there is not the same kind of mother-offspring relationship that is found in a flock of sheep, nor do there seem to be the patterns of aggressive relationships that are a feature of many higher animal societies. The bond that ties ant to ant and bee to bee is *trophallaxis*—the complex ritual of giving and receiving food. A successful forager brings a load of food back to the colony not for her personal use but for the use of the whole community.

When a foraging bee returns she offers food to another worker, who in turn solicits it from the forager by holding out her tongue to receive a portion that is exuded from the forager's mouth. Then the pair part and the forager goes to another bee. Even within the hive, bees pass food on and receive it back, so that there is a constant stream of food being passed around the hive through the mouths and honey stomachs of the individual members of the colony.

This food-exchanging behavior is instinctive. It is inherited by the bees. If one of them is confronted with only the heads of workers she will go up to them and tap and stroke them with her antennae in an attempt to obtain food. Even a model head made from a blob of modeling clay will evoke this behavior if it has two little bits of wire stuck into it to

Ants spend much time touching one anothers' bodies with their antennae and soliciting food from, or offering food to, other adults within the colony. The two ants shown are exchanging food in a ritual called trophallaxis. In strengthening the bond between individual insects trophallaxis plays a role much like that of grooming in mammal societies.

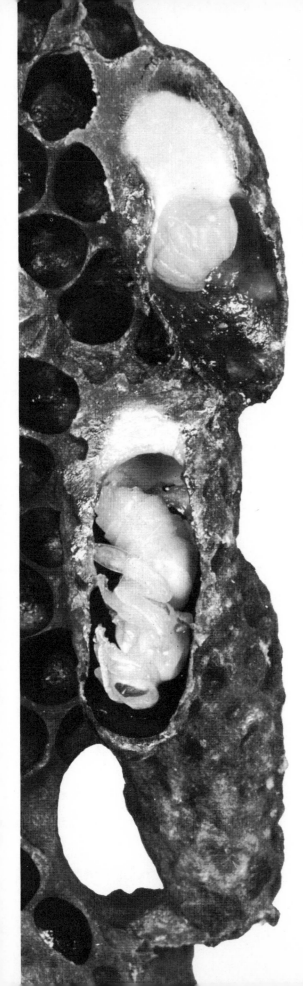

Left: The two queen cells shown here are much larger than cells that contain worker-bee larvae. Royal jelly, on which the queen larvae feed, surrounds the larva in the upper cell and is also visible at the top of the lower cell. Above: A queen bee inspects brood cells made by workers, which are responsible for feeding the larvae and for keeping the hive clean. Workers determine, by the form and quantity of food that they put into the larval cells, whether queens or workers will be produced. Any apparent failings in the "reigning" queen will immediately result in the construction of new queen cells.

represent antennae. This shows that the antennae are the important recognition feature. They act as a stimulus for the soliciting behavior.

The food exchange is carried out very quickly. In one hive six foragers were allowed to collect a tablespoonful of sugar water that contained a radioactive marker. Twenty-nine hours later well over half the bees in the hive were radioactive.

This food exchange forms a ready-made circulation system for passing chemical substances from bee to bee. And it is through this that the production of the queens is controlled. Different adult workers and queens are produced as a result of being fed the necessary diet by the workers. As long as an active queen is in the hive, no others are produced. But as soon as she begins to fail in any way, the workers begin to build the characteristic queen cells. These are somewhat larger than the usual cells and only queens are reared in them.

Queen-cell building is triggered off when the supply of *queen substance* going round the hive in the trophallaxis stream begins to decrease. This substance is made in the glands of the queen's head, and as she licks her body she coats it with the substance. This is then licked off her body by the attendant workers who are continually grooming the queen. They pass on some of it to others, and these bees to others, and so on.

If the queen and some workers are kept away from the rest of the hive by a gauze fence through which the bees can pass food, circulation of the queen substance can continue throughout the colony. But if a second fence is put up just far enough from the first to prevent food exchange between the two parts of the hive, queen cells will soon be built in the part without a queen. The queen's "power" over the hive depends upon her queen substance. While it circulates through the hive she influences the behavior of the workers so that they do not produce successor queens.

The passing of food between insects probably has an important effect on the ways social insects recognize each other. Each colony of ants, each hive of bees, each nest of wasps, and each mound of termites has its own special odor that every individual member of the group bears on its body. It is by this odor that members are distinguished from outsiders when they attempt to enter the colony—the odor is the badge of recognition.

Ants trying to enter a strange nest will bear the wrong odor. They will be attacked and, often, killed. The guards at a beehive examine each bee that lands on the landing board in front of the hive entrance. They are constantly on the alert, standing in a characteristic posture and lunging at every bee that comes near as well as at the shadows of bees flying by. Strange bees may land at the hive, mistaking it for their own. But the strangers are quite submissive when manhandled by the guards. With abdomen tucked under their bodies, they allow their wings and legs to be pulled off by the guards, who then push them over the edge of the landing board. A trespasser often "strops" her tongue while she is being examined. This action resembles tongue cleaning, which is part of normal behavior; but the action is performed at a more rapid speed. The stropping demonstrates the conflict between submission and resistance that is dominating the

trespasser's behavior. If the intruders are robber bees intending to steal honey, they struggle when the guards hold them. They are swiftly rolled into a ball by the guards and stung to death. The odor that distinguishes one colony from another may result because all the individuals in a specific colony are eating food that is gathered by only a few members and is passed from mouth to mouth.

The work of a honeybee hive is very elaborate. The bees make the comb with plates of wax secreted from glands on their abdomens. The queen then lays an egg in each cell. When the larvae hatch they are fed with honey and pollen and with the secretions from the glands of some of the workers. A fully grown larva is enclosed in its cell. When it changes into an adult bee it bites its way out. The workers have many tasks in addition to gathering food and guarding the hive. They spend much of their time tidying the hive and in fanning the air with their wings to cool and ventilate it.

All this work is carried out instinctively. As a general rule, the work that an adult bee does depends upon her age. She tidies the hive during the first few days of her life, then feeds the larvae until about the 10th day when she begins to build comb. Around the 15th day, she turns to guard duties, then leaves the hive to gather food after the 20th day. The relationship between age and job is not rigid. If the need arises for a bigger foraging force, bees younger than usual will join it.

As the whole colony of the social insects is directed toward reproduction, it is not sur-

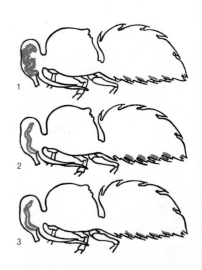

prising that the work of food collection is carried out very efficiently. For example, ants often lay a scent trail when they return to the colony after gathering food. Other members of the colony can then find the food source without delay—and they in turn will reinforce the trail on their way homeward. But as soon as the food at this source begins to diminish the amount of scent laid by each forager diminishes also.

A honeybee is able to learn the position of her food supplies. She learns to recognize the appearance of the flowers she visits; she also learns to distinguish the landmarks along her route from the hive. Remarkably, she is also able to communicate all this knowledge to the other foragers when she returns to the hive. This she does by dancing, and she is followed by two or three other bees as she performs.

The bees dance on the vertical face of the comb hanging in the hive. If the food is less than 100 yards away the bee walks round in a circle, then turns and retraces her steps to her starting point. This is the round dance—it indicates merely that food is nearby. If the food is farther away than 100 yards, the bee dances in a figure resembling a circle bisected by a diameter (see diagram). She starts by pacing out the diameter line, then turns left (or right) and dances out a semicircle by returning to the other end of the diameter. Then she moves up the diameter line again, and turning right (or left) at the end completes the other half of the circle.

For the purpose of the dance, the direction of the sun from the hive is represented by an imaginary line running vertically from the bottom to the top of the comb, the sun's position being at the top. The diameter line represents the direction of the food in relation to the direction of the sun. So that, as she moves along the diameter, if the bee goes straight up the comb, the food lies in the direction of the sun. If she moves straight down, it lies in the direction opposite to the sun's position. If the direction of the food is at a certain angle to the sun's direction, this is indicated in the dance by the angle of the diameter from the vertical. As she moves along the diameter the bee waggles her abdomen from side to side. The more she waggles, the longer it takes her to complete the dance. The duration of the dance is related to the distance of the food—the longer the dance, the farther the food.

The bee dance is a striking example of communication between animals. The bee conveys information in much the same way as a human does when he draws a map. Human societies, have more in common with societies of ants and bees than with those of most higher animals. The fundamental difference between human and insect societies is that the insects' activities are largely instinctive. Even the most complicated patterns of behavior—like the bee dance—are limited in their extent and variety by instinct. Insects have little of the ability to adapt their behavior to changes in the environment that distinguishes man from other species.

Right: Worker bees indicate to each other the direction and distance of food supplies by performing a dance on the vertical surface of the honeycomb. The dance consists of a more or less circular figure bisected by a diameter line. The angle between this diameter line and an imaginary vertical line on the wall of the comb corresponds to the horizontal angle between the direction of the food source and the direction of the sun when both are viewed from the hive. The distance of the food is indicated by the frequency with which the bee waggles her abdomen during the dance—the greater the distance, the higher the number of waggles.

Left: The main stages of a worker bee's life are accompanied by changes in glands of head and abdomen. (1) Until 10 days old the worker feeds new larvae with fluid protein secreted by her head glands. (2) For the next 10 days she builds cells. The wax glands in her abdomen grow larger, the head glands shrink. (3) After the twentieth day she gathers food and both wax and head glands diminish in size.

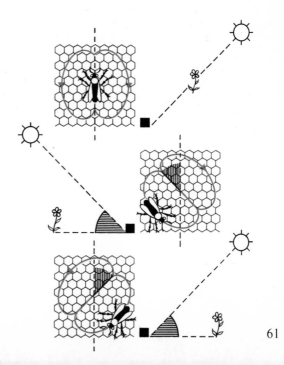

In the breeding season many adult male animals establish territories in which they can mate and in which the young can be born and raised in safety. The male will vigorously defend his territory against other male (and often female) intruders of his own species. In the photograph the European fox on the log is about to attack another that has wandered into his territory.

4. Home Ground

In the mating season most birds and many fish leave their flocks and schools and withdraw in pairs to limited areas which the male defends against other males of his own kind. These limited areas become the "private" territories of the pairs. The main purpose they serve, but not the only one, is to provide a place where the animals can mate in peace. This may seem an unnecessary precaution, but courtship behavior is an elaborate and important ritual designed to link the reproductive drives of male and female. It is essential that once started, mating should be interrupted as little as possible, and preferably not at all.

The claiming of territory may also serve to define an area in which the owner can feed in comparative safety. In a feeding territory the owner fights off intruders of his own species but admits other animals, just as in a territory set up for mating. Keeping out animals of the same species ensures that competition for the same sort of food is kept under control. Animals of other species can be admitted because their preferences for food—and for mates—are different.

As a general rule, the territories of two species with similar food preferences do not overlap. This has the effect of spacing the animals fairly evenly over the whole area in

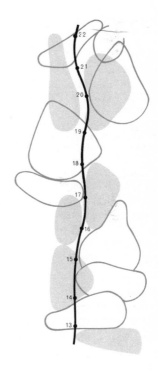

This diagram shows the territories of several individuals of two "competing" bird species—wood pewee (blue lines) and least fly-catcher (blue shaded area)—flanking a forest path.

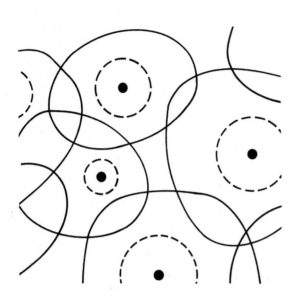

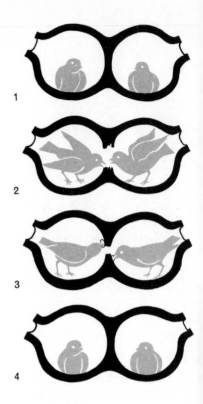

Each territory is established within a home range — the area habitually traveled by an animal in search of food or a mate. The diagram shows a typical relationship between territories (within broken lines) and home ranges (within solid lines) of individuals of the same species. The dots represent nest sites.

An experiment on cliff swallows with adjoining mud nests. (1) The birds brooding their eggs. While both birds were absent, the wall between the nests was broken and, on their return (2), the swallows fought. Later (3) they repaired the wall and (4), resumed brooding. Their territories seem to be limited to the nests.

which they can live, so that all of it is in use and none of it is overcrowded. Meat-eating animals such as lions, that need wide hunting areas, have large territories so that the families are spaced far apart. In contrast, grass-eating animals whose food is easier to obtain, usually have much smaller territories.

Spacing-out of this kind can be very important for animals that depend on camouflage for protection. If they are huddled together when a predator sights them they are all open to attack. But if they are well spaced out it is probable that the predator will find only single animals while the rest remain protected by their likeness to the surroundings. Among ground-nesting birds the survival of the species is often largely dependent on the fact that either the eggs or the mother birds that sit on them blend with the background. Here spacing-out can be very important.

In the spring, birds begin to lay claim to their territories. Generally a male stakes his claim by singing his "advertisement" song from a tall tree or a telephone pole, which becomes his song post. This warns other males that he is in possession. The extent of the territory is then determined by the success of his attacks on any other males that attempt to cross an imaginary boundary. The remarkable thing about these boundaries, which are seldom obvious to us, is that they do not follow the line of some striking feature such as a hedge. Yet they are just as real for a bird — or a fish, for that matter — as if the territory were bounded by high walls.

Many mammals do mark their territory. Antelope, for example, have glands on their faces which they rub against the ends of twigs. The strong-smelling substance left on the twig serves as a notice of ownership. Cali-

Above: A male swan driving other swans from his territory. Though usually invisible to the human eye, the borders of each territory are clearly defined by the owner, who usually claims as large an area as he can effectively defend against rivals of the same species.

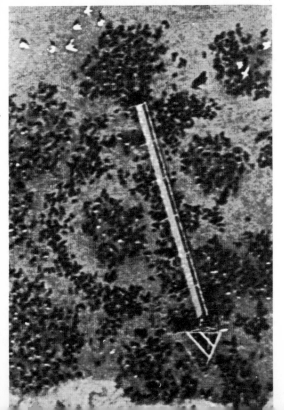

Left: Territorial division is apparent in this colony of fur seals on St. Paul Island, Alaska. To the left of the observation walk a dominant male patrols the circular path he has cleared around his harem of females. Around the outer edge of the path is a crowd of seal pups.

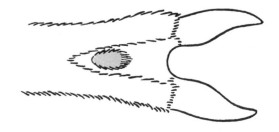

Animals advertise ownership of territory in a variety of ways. The red deer above marks the ground, bushes, and trees with secretions from glands near its eyes. Muntjac, small deer found in south-east Asia, have glands (right) on their feet that are used for the same purpose.

fornian ground squirrels mark stones with a secretion from their dorsal glands. Civets and ocelots use piles of excreta, while many other members of the cat family use urine. Hippopotami use dung and urine to establish their right to a territory.

Outside its own territory an animal seems to be at a disadvantage and an intruder never reacts as strongly to threats as the owner of territory does. A very aggressive dog, for instance, that attacks all visitors to the house in which he lives, may be quite docile when off his own ground. Human beings, too, are often more self-confident at home than elsewhere. Perhaps this accounts for the old saying that "a man's home is his castle"! The feeling of inferiority that arises when off one's home ground may be one of the reasons why challenges to territorial rights seldom result in bloodshed. In the shifting movements of threat and counterthreat, animals are con-

tinually moving off their own territory and thus losing some of their belligerence.

The exceptions to this rule usually concern fights that take place over mates. The ferocity of fights for mates between bull sea-elephants has to be seen to be believed. These huge animals fiercely protect their harems of females against other bulls, and if an intruder makes a challenging approach the owner of the harem attacks, using his great canine teeth to inflict deep wounds on his rival. On the whole, however, fights almost to the death do not flare up over territory.

Avoiding Fights to a Finish

A real fight is often avoided when one animal gives up. He does this by adopting what is called a *submissive posture*. A black-headed gull will greet an intruder by straightening his neck upward, holding his beak pointed down-

The diagram above shows a typical layout of neighboring territories of hippopotamuses. These animals make their homes (black dots) in the river, shown in blue, where they mate, give birth, and hide in the event of danger. From the short section of river favored by several family groups the territories broaden out into large, pear-shaped areas. The circles and red trails mark one specific territory.

Above: Grooming among prairie dogs commonly follows identification encounters between two members of the same neighborhood group.

ward and his wings just raised. His neck feathers are also slightly ruffled. From this position he can, if necessary, aim a blow at his opponent with his outstretched wings. The intruder adopts a similar stance. Then the two birds walk beside each other, or circle like boxers waiting for an opening. But the attack rarely takes place, for one of the birds—usually the intruder—will suddenly turn his head and beak away from the other. This is a sign of submission, whereupon the other bird ceases to threaten. If his first threats are unsuccessful, the owner of the territory may try other postures and even pull at grass in a way which is very like that of pulling at feathers on an opponent's wing in an actual fight. Usually, by this time, the intruder has given up and gone away.

It is interesting that submission often involves behavior in which the animal sets aside his weapon, as when the gull turns his beak away from his opponent. Occasionally an animal may show submission by offering a vulnerable part of his body to his opponent, as a submissive dog does when he exposes the scruff of his neck. In all this behavior there seems to be a conflict between the desire to attack and the desire to run away. The gestures waver between threat and appeasement until one or other gets the upper hand.

Boundary encounters in a prairie-dog township are often strongly marked by this alternation of threat and appeasement. When two animals see each other they approach crouched down on their bellies, flicking their tails in the air as they creep forward. The conspicuous black tip of their raised tails makes this posture particularly obvious. If they belong to the same neighborhood group, they will "kiss," with open lips and bared teeth. Set in this way their mouths are in a position to bite—a sign of potential aggression. If they

Left: Prairie dogs are constantly on the look-out for interlopers from other neighborhood groups. In (1) and (2) the animals are from the same group and exchange the identification "kiss." The tail-raising ceremony (3) occurs between members of different groups. Each tries to bite his opponent's rump. Between each ceremony the animals separate for a moment (4), then renew the ritualistic contest, which usually ends when one retreats, ceding a few feet of territory to the other.

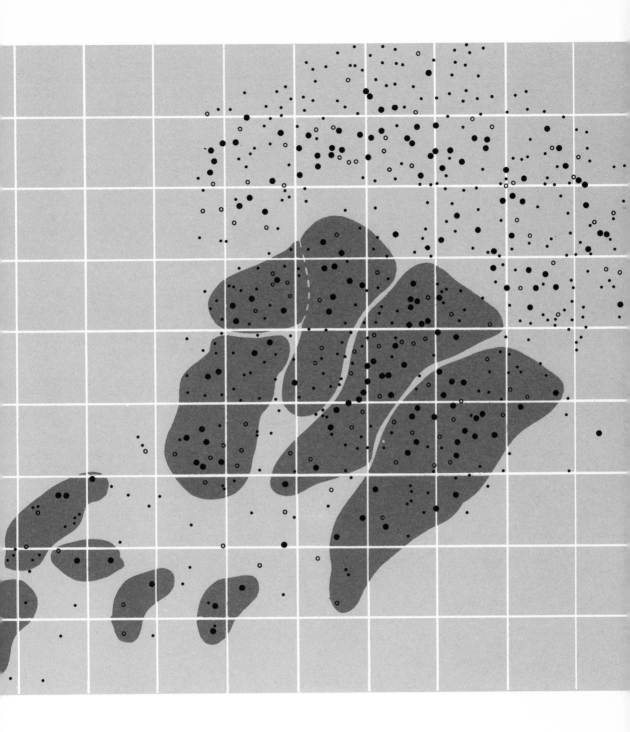

Map of about five acres of prairie dog township (each square being 50 feet wide). The neighborhood groups are shown in dark brown. The smaller brown areas are new territories being colonized by emigrating adults. The large dots show positions of large, active burrows; the circles indicate smaller burrows; the small dots are holes without entrance mounds.

are enemies, from different groups, they "freeze" a short distance apart. Then one turns and presents its raised tail to the other, at the same time displaying its anal glands. The other comes nearer and does the same. This alternation continues until one bites the rump of the other. The bitten one then retreats a few feet and the display begins once more. The "fight" is over when one of the animals gives up, perhaps because he has shifted too far into the other's territory and has lost some of his aggression.

The territory owner may then dash to one of the entrance mounds where, standing on his hind legs and crying out so forcibly that he jumps into the air, he gives his territorial call. This is as much an advertisement of territory ownership as the song of a meadowlark, sung from a fence post.

Some fish behave remarkably like many birds. They depend very largely on vision for recognition of each other's signals. They are colored in ways that are highly significant to other fish. They build nests, and they mark out territories. When put into a tank together, male fish of the same species will often fight each other for a territory whose boundaries are just as real to the fish (and just as invisible to us) as those of birds. Here, too, territorial boundaries are decided by fighting and threatening. For instance, a male stickleback will defend an area around the pit he has begun to make as a foundation for a nest. If another breeding male showing the distinctive, red mating coloring comes into the territory, he attacks him and chases him away. As soon as the pursuit takes him over the border of his territory, he becomes less aggressive and his opponent then chases him back. The two fish shuttle back and forth for some time until one or other tires and gives up. The owner may also display aggressively at his frontier, keeping his nose down, his ventral spines erect, and flicking his fins and tail. He will even dis-

In the breeding season the male stickleback develops a red coloring on its underside and attacks similarly marked males that enter his territory. In tests, crude models, dissimilar in shape from the stickleback but bearing the red coloring on the underside, were always attacked; an exact copy of the fish (top), but without the coloring, was not attacked.

Encounter between two cichlids defending adjacent territories. They first swim in a circle, nose to tail, threatening each other by expanding their throat regions and spreading their fins. Then the more aggressive of the cichlids butts his rival who, defeated, prevents further attack by adopting a submissive attitude similar to that of a female entering a male's territory.

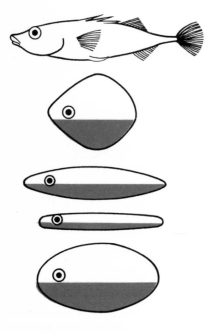

Switching from their normal brown color to a deep black, two gobies, disputing territory, circle and butt each other in a manner similar to the cichlids. Encounters between well-matched gobies may result in serious wounds for both, since the ritual butting soon gives way to biting.

Male fiddler-crab defending his burrow against an intruder. The crab's territory includes an area of shore around the burrow. He advertises his ownership by waving his large right claw somewhat in the way a fiddler draws a bow across the strings of a violin.

play like this to his own reflection in a mirror.

Cichlid fish, fresh-water perch of the tropics, use their tails to beat water at their opponents. Two competing males stay side by side with dorsal fins erect and gill covers raised. Each turns its tail toward his opponent and, with vigorous strokes, makes a current of water that strikes the other fish and is sensed by its lateral line system.

Vertebrate animals such as mammals, birds, and fish are not the only creatures that mark out territories. This sort of behavior is also common among certain insects and crustaceans. Male dragonflies, for example, will defend sections of a river bank against other males of their species and, indeed, against other species of dragonfly. They are so aggressive that after grappling with the trespasser they may eat him. What purpose a dragonfly's territory serves is not clear.

Territories established by fiddler crabs are much more like those of birds, with the male

crab defending an area of shore around the burrow into which he lures the female. He signals his ownership by a peculiar waving of the big claw which gives these crabs their name. He raises the claw and brings it down again in an abrupt movement as though it were operated by a spring. The large claw is also used in duelling rituals in which a fiddler crab defends his territory or his right to a mate against an intruding male. Fiddler-crab territory may serve the same purposes as bird territory, for it provides a place for mating and causes the animals to spread out, thus lessening the chances that they may be taken as prey.

Mapping Animal Territory

Not much is known about the organization of territory or whether particular parts of it are used for particular purposes. Apart from the nest itself and a favorite singing spot or two, no part of a bird's territory seems to be used for a special purpose. But mammals, and particularly herbivores (plant-eaters), often have an elaborate system of tracks that criss-cross their territory, connecting different points where they defecate, and have water holes, rubbing trees, and so forth. The hub of the territory is the main home, where the owner generally sleeps. Herbivorous animals do not usually feed around this base, and the long grass that is left serves as cover. It is quite common for animals not to eat in the immediate neighborhood of their main home. Near their own "doorstep" anteaters may even burrow into termite nests but leave the inmates unharmed, though they feed on termites in other nests. And carnivores, both birds and mammals, often seem to kill their prey only at places beyond a certain distance from their home or nest. These places, however, usually occur within the animals' home range (see diagram on page 64).

The elaborate behavior associated with establishing a territory confirms its importance to animals. It seems that there are times when it is necessary for the animal not to be part of a flock, but to be apart and on its own in order to ensure a good food supply, uninterrupted mating, or full use of camouflage.

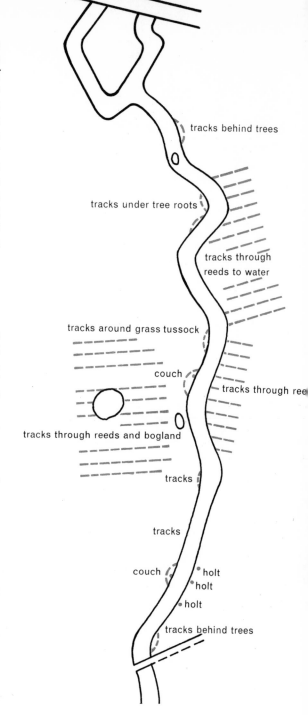

Map of otter territories along a stretch of river in Wales. Broken lines represent tracks of otters. Couches are usually concealed resting places used at day and night. Holts are dens used for sleeping and for bearing young. Even during breeding periods, males and females commonly live apart. Although essentially aquatic, otters often make journeys away from water.

72

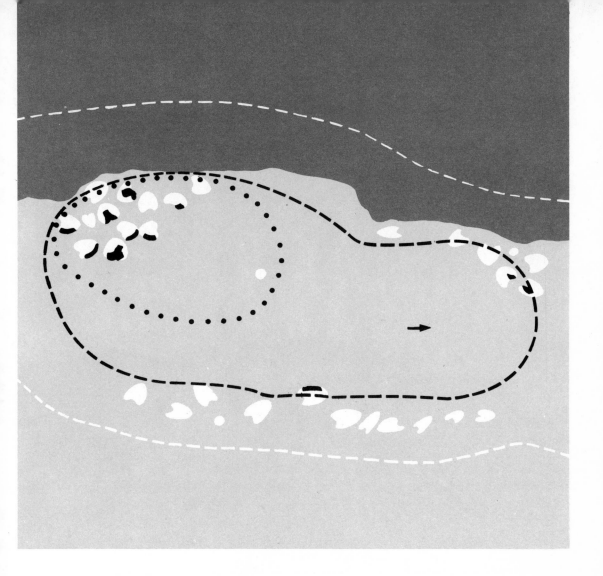

Above: Plan of a male dragonfly's territory. The dark area represents the river bank, the light area the river, and the arrow the direction of the current. The white broken line encloses the mating area, the black broken line the defended territory. The black patches on floating leaves (shown in white) are sites where females have laid eggs. The white patch at the right-hand end of the egg-laying territory represents a flower that the male uses as a settling base.

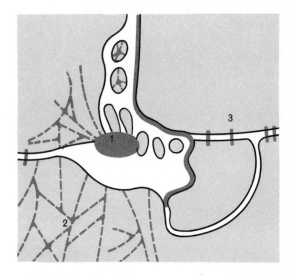

Right: A beaver pond near Voronezh, U.S.S.R. The land is shown in light brown, the beaver constructions in dark brown. (1) is the beavers' house. (2) are subterranean canals on the bank of the pond and on the small islands. (3) are dams, including one that stretches along more than one third of the pond bank and has effectively blocked the outflow of water into two streams.

73

Courtship is largely instinctive among most animals.
Each species has a predetermined pattern of behavior.
Among some it is a long and complex ritual, among
others brief and sketchy. But the main purpose of
courtship is the same for all — to synchronize and
intensify the male and female's drive to mate. The
gorgeous display of this peacock stresses the importance
of the first courtship act — mutual recognition between
a pair of the same species.

5. Courtship and Instinct

All animal species reproduce themselves in some way at some time in their lives. Some can do so without the aid of the opposite sex, either by budding off pieces of themselves that take on a separate existence or by laying eggs that do not need to be fertilized.

Certain other species can reproduce without intimate contact between the two sexes, as in the cases where the male discharges his sperm and the female her eggs into a common medium such as a pond or the sea. In these cases the male and female breeding cycles must be timed to ensure that there is sperm available when there are eggs ready for fertilizing, but there is no need for male and female to meet.

Courtship, however, involves the actual meeting and mating of a pair of animals. It is important that the two animals are of the same species, otherwise the mating will usually come to nothing. Or if offspring do result they will usually be infertile — that is, incapable of reproducing themselves. Much of courtship, therefore, is concerned with mutual recognition, and failure to recognize often results in failure to mate. A good example of

this is what happens when attempts are made to mate a white stork with a black one. The white stork has a greeting ceremony in which it bends its head backward to touch its back, then brings it forward and downward, clapping its beak. Another white stork would do the same in reply and mutual recognition would follow. But a black stork greets another in quite a different way, moving its head from side to side while making a whispering noise. When a black stork is put with a white one, each fails to recognize the other as a potential mate.

Correct recognition is particularly important where a number of different species that look alike are crowded together. In such conditions we may find special recognition aids. For example, in the islands of the Azores, where there are few other small birds, the song of the chaffinch is rather simple; on the European mainland, where there are many other small birds, the chaffinch's song carries extra trills. This song is learned, and, because of its complexity, it stands out clearly against the background of other bird songs.

The Timing of Courtship

There is another reason for the complicated and conspicuous behavior of courting animals. Mating can be successful only when the two animals are both in the right physiological state. That is, when the blood contains certain hormones that will ensure the production of fertile eggs in the female and sperm in the male. It follows that if courtship is to result in successful mating timing is important. Indeed, this may be so even among species where there is no actual sexual intercourse. A male newt, for instance, deposits his sperm in a small jelly-like packet on the bottom of a pond; the female picks it up in her cloaca and her eggs are fertilized by the sperm. If the female were not in readiness to pick up the packet, it would be useless for the male to leave it. In fact he ensures that the packet is deposited only near an "interested" female by performing an elaborate courtship dance.

Among birds, the function of courtship is perhaps even more important, for with these animals the body's final preparation for egg production depends upon a series of actions and circumstances, such as courtship display and the availability of a nest site. In addition, the choice of territory as a place free from interference undoubtedly plays a part in ensuring the success of mating.

Most animals do not court at all times of the year but come into "season" annually. Thus most birds breed only in spring, Breeding time seems to be brought on by the increase in the hours of daylight, which starts in early spring. In fact, birds can be brought into breeding conditions earlier than usual by providing them with increasing periods of artificial light each day during the very early part of the year. The seasonal timing of breeding is of great importance. Greater length of day gives birds a longer time in which to find food for their young, so that spring is the appropriate time for mating to take place.

In both males and females hormones are responsible for the sex drive that brings about courtship. But the hormones are produced in response to the longer daylight hours. When the change of length of day is recorded by the bird's eye, the pituitary gland at the base of the brain secretes hormones that cause eggs to ripen in females and great numbers of sperms to be formed in males.

Above: A female black-headed gull (at right in upper photograph) is attracted by a displaying male. On nearing the male, however, she becomes "anxious" about the encounter and eventually rejects him by turning away (lower photograph). In a moment or two she will walk or fly away.

In contrast to the courtship of birds, the courtship of pigs and many other mammals shows no elaborate rituals.

Above: Chin-resting by the bull tests the cow's readiness to mate. If the cow is unreceptive she moves away. Some male antelopes use chin-resting to guide the female to their mating territories.

In tropical countries many species of birds breed after the rains have a new growth of green plants to supply an abundance of food and nesting materials. There it is the rains that act as the trigger rather than the length of day which changes very little from season to season.

Courtship Behavior in Mammals

With many mammals courtship can occur only when the female is in *estrus* — that is, when her ovaries contain ripe eggs that can be fertilized. At other times she is not receptive. Her behavior is controlled by hormones that come from the ovaries and other glands, which in turn have been responsible for bringing her into estrus. She cannot be in estrus while she is pregnant nor, usually, for a time after the birth, when she is nursing her young. During these times the particular hormones responsible for sexual behavior are not being produced.

Mammals do not engage in the elaborate courtship behavior that is common among birds. A cow will refuse to let a bull mate with her except when she is in estrus, which occurs for only a few hours every few weeks. The bull can detect a cow that is soon to come into estrus, perhaps by her scent or by something in her behavior that is not obvious to us. At this time he "guards" her, standing parallel to her, nose to tail. Although he may try to mate at this time, the cow moves away and mating does not take place.

When the cow is in full estrus the bull becomes greatly excited. He may paw the ground or dig it with his horns, tossing dirt over his back. Then he moves behind the cow and places his chin and throat on her rump. If she is still unreceptive she moves away, otherwise she stands still and allows him to mate with her. Similar chin-resting behavior is found among some species of antelope. The male uses this position to guide the female into a special mating territory.

Smell plays an important part in the behavior of mammals and the courting bull may appear to depend largely upon scent. However, experiments suggest that the main stimuli to which the bull is responding are visual — the shape of the cow, for example, being very important.

However, many mammals do use scent in their courtship behavior, sometimes in rather surprising ways. Male wild rabbits, for instance, will urinate on the female they are courting, and male porcupines do the same, while a moose will mark with urine the area where he is awaiting the female. We saw earlier how mammals frequently use urine and secretions from special glands to mark possession of a territory. In a sense, the use here is to mark the female as the possession of the male.

Display in Birds

It is among birds, with their strutting and posturing, that we often find bizarre possibilities of courtship behavior. With few exceptions, it is the male bird who plays the active part in courtship and who has the more beautiful plumage. Some of the more exotic male birds have special breeding plumage that enables them to put on flamboyant displays in order to persuade a female to mate with them. Once again, however, it cannot be too strongly stressed that courtship is a mutual affair. For example, it is just as important for the female crested grebe to raise herself out of the water with her "ears" of feathers erect in response to the male, as it is for the male himself to carry out his courtship performance.

Perhaps the most striking courtship displays are to be seen among the birds of paradise that live in New Guinea. The female is usually a brown and somewhat drab bird, but the plumage of the male is brighter than that of the peacock. Though he is only a small to medium-sized bird he is made to look deceptively large by his erected plumes, and often by a long tail, and his colors are splendid.

The blue bird of paradise, for example, has blue wings, and underparts variously colored in blue, azure, and black, with tints of chestnut. His tail is black with two long central feathers that broaden at the end. When he

Both male and female crested grebe are active in courtship. (1) Female adopts "seeking" attitude. Head shaking (2) and the "cat" position (3) are used by male and female. (4) After diving the male surfaces and stretches up out of the water; the female is still in position (3). In the "penguin dance" (5) both birds stretch upward and present each other with bits of plant.

Blackcocks (left) and sage grouse (right) display in their communal courtship areas. Several other flocking birds also have such courtship areas, to which groups of males of the same species return every year in the early spring. Here they engage in dominance encounters that establish priority in the choice of mates, who may arrive at the areas several weeks after the males. Among groups of sage grouse the most dominant male will do as much as 80 per cent of the mating.

displays, he stands perched with plumage slightly raised and wings quivering. He bows first to one side, then to the other. Back and forth he goes, each time making a deeper bow until finally he touches the branch with his beak. Then suddenly he swings around the bough to hang upside down displaying all his finery, with wings spread out and plumes and breast feathers fully erected. For a while he hangs quivering. Then, at a movement of his breast feathers, a band of black edged with flame-red appears across his body.

The hanging display is found in many, but not all, birds of paradise. What is remarkable is the striking transformation that the bird sometimes undergoes. The "superb" bird of paradise seems scarcely worthy of his name when seen perching quietly on a branch. Admittedly he is a splendid velvety black with a beautiful sheen to him, especially at the top of his head where the feathers are blue-green, or at his breast, which shines iridescently, or on his back with its double cape of feathers. Yet "superb" may seem too strong a word to describe him. But in display, all his colors are shown off to full advantage as he fans out his cape to provide a background for his head, and spreads his breast feathers sideways to flaunt their luminous blue. He beats his wings against the bough, making a sound, and then gives a harsh scream, revealing the bright yellow lining of his gaping mouth. For a while he is indeed superb. Then as suddenly as he started, he folds his feathers together, lowers his cape, and returns to his less impressive normal appearance.

Male birds of certain other species have different sorts of special display equipment. The frigate bird of the tropical seas, expands a great scarlet sac beneath his throat, lowers his wings, and claps his beak while calling "wow, wow, wow." The display of male sage grouse also includes the inflation of air sacs, and the birds look very puffed up as they strut about with heads thrown back, wings extended, and spiky tails erect. Every so often they deflate the sac with a "plop."

Male sage grouse of the western Great Plains are birds with distinct "traditions," for they meet together each season in display areas which have been used for that purpose for generations. When the male sage grouse meet for their communal display they first

Right: Ruffs also engage in dominance contests — known as "arena behavior" — in order to establish mating priorities in their communal areas. The contests seldom lead to injury. Although the most dominant males attract the most mates, it is the females that select their mates, usually by pecking at the raised neck-feathers of the male of their choice. These gaudy feathers have no use other than in courtship.

spend some time in deciding which is to be "king of the hill"—the dominant male who will mate most frequently with the females that approach. When the display begins, the females come up to the posturing males to pick out their mates. No doubt crowding together for display makes the presence of the males more conspicuous so that the females can find them easily. The intensity of each male bird's display is heightened by association with the other males. This is an example of facilitation, described in Chapter 3.

Competitive fighting for male dominance also takes place among ruffs, a bird found in eastern Europe. They gather on the same "hill," or display ground, year after year. In the breeding season, the males develop a splendid ruff, which when erected looks like the great starched collar worn by an Elizabethan courtier. With ruffs erect, the males circle and spar, jumping in the air. Occasion-

The lyre-bird's beautiful tail spread consists of three groups of display feathers—the large, horizontal lyre-feathers, two vertical feathers, and 12 branching feathers forming the "veil." At rest the tail is flat like that of a pheasant.

ally they peck at one another, but without doing serious injury. Here, too, sexual readiness is doubtless increased by facilitation as each member of the group witnesses the dancing and displaying of the others. The females (called reeves) watch the strange staccato display before selecting a mate. The pair may mate on the hill itself but more often the female flies off a little way with the ruff following. Although the members of the group display together, each male has already trodden down a patch of grass on the hill for his own use.

Another bird that prepares a dancing ground is the male Jackson's whidah that live on the African grasslands. The whidah prepares its individual patch by treading down a ring of grass with a tuft left standing in the middle. He protects this ground in a territory that extends from six to ten feet in radius around the tuft. His display in the ring attracts one of the females who fly over as the males dance. When the female alights, the male dances around the ring, leaping on the side away from the female but playing "peek-a-boo" around the tuft, darting out to flaunt his tail at her. Often this display must be repeated in front of several females before one will allow him to mate with her.

Female Submission

In almost half the total number of bird species, male and female are outwardly very similar. In these cases, the female has no badge of special plumage to mark her out, and she must identify herself by her behavior. When she enters the male's territory he may start by threatening her. Her response is to adopt a submissive posture instead of the aggressive one that another male would show.

The courting of rooks (crow-like birds of Europe) follows this pattern. Rooks gather and court in large flocks as early as November. A male will approach a female with his wings drooping and his tail fanned, then bring his head forward and down several times. If the female accepts his attention she takes up a crouching position, holding her wings extended and quivering slightly. The two may remain together after this but they will not mate until later on. Real courtship does not begin until the end of February of the follow-

Pair of crossbills engaged in courtship feeding. Nourishment, as such, is not the intention since only small amounts of food are involved. In begging for food, the female mimics the behavior of a nestling and thereby helps to subdue the male's aggression. The passing of food from mouth to mouth may also serve to lessen the fear of physical contact (even with others of their kind) that is common to many species of birds.

A spider common in England, courts the female by offering her a fly wrapped in his thread. If receptive, the female takes and eats the gift. While she is thus occupied, the male mates with her. If he fails to present a gift, the male may himself be eaten by the larger female. Lacking fresh prey, male may wrap and present the empty carcass of a fly.

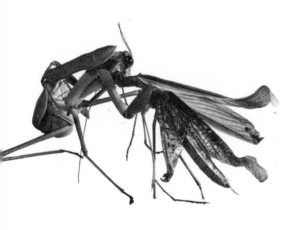

Less fortunate than spider above, this male mantis is devoured by the larger and heavier female with whom he has just mated.

ing year. Then the male brings food to the female. In response she behaves as if she were a young bird: She crouches down and quivers her wings and stretches her neck to receive the food which is pushed into her bill.

Courtship feeding of this sort occurs among a number of bird species. Although the female bird may later be truly dependent upon her mate for food while she is sitting on the eggs, at this stage the feeding is no more than a token. For example, during courtship a male robin offers his mate only one insect, but when feeding his young he carries a beak full. The actual feeding of the female is obviously not his intention. Yet, like the female rook, the female English robin shows remarkably infantile behavior during courtship feeding. She will even imitate the call made by a hungry young bird begging for food.

In fact, the female bird is behaving in the most submissive way she can, for in imitating the young bird she is acting out the stage in a bird's life history when it is least likely to be attacked, since fledglings are neither rivals for mates nor a threat to a male's position in a dominance pattern. Her submission appears to subdue the male's aggression—which is essential if he is to take part in a mutual ceremony whose result is to bring the pair into readiness for mating.

Courtship feeding also occurs among insects. In some species of flies the male offers the female the prey it has caught, wound in

The male stickleback, *usually aggressive to male or female within his territory, recognizes and is attracted to the egg-carrying female by the shape of her swollen body. She emphasizes this shape by raising her head and tail (1), while the male dances in a zig-zag in front of her. Then he leads her to the nest he has prepared (2).*

Many species have bright colors and patterns that they display during courtship and at other times. A typical example is the tropical cichlid fish, which has a black spot ringed by yellow-green on its gill cover. When the fish is being aggressive the spot is shown off by raising the gill covers so that they stand out on either side of the head. Fish can perform movements in three dimensions. They swim up and down in the water as well as to and fro and from side to side. And finally many of them mark out territories into which they attract a female and in which the eggs are laid.

Even the details of fish courtship behavior may be like that of birds. A female cichlid, for example, becomes submissive when she enters the territory of a male. He threatens her by erecting his dorsal fin, coming at her head on with gill covers raised, or beating water at her with his tail. Her response is to remain passive, with dorsal fin collapsed. When fully ready for courtship, she submits to the male's butting but nimbly avoids most of the blows. In answer to his behavior she makes little display, and so makes herself clearly recognizable as a female.

The way in which a male stickleback identifies a female has been studied, and we can say exactly what features she has that cause a male to behave differently toward her than he would toward another male. Before going on to see what these features are, we need to

silky strands. In other species the bundle he offers may contain only flower petals, and in yet others it is quite empty. There is also courtship feeding among spiders, but it is certainly not associated with submissive behavior on the part of the female. In some spiders the female is so aggressive that she may attack and eat the male. In these cases the male may offer her a fly to distract her during mating. This seems to give him some assurance that he himself will not be consumed.

Water Courtships

The courtship behavior of fishes often shows a strong resemblance to that of birds.

The highly developed courtship ceremony of these and other cichlids includes ritual "mouth fighting" immediately before mating.

Below: In the intensely active courtship and nuptial ceremony of Siamese fighting fish the male and female circle and seemingly intertwine at high speed (1). The eggs emerge from the female (2) and the male fertilizes them as they sink toward the bottom. Then he takes the eggs in his mouth (3), carries them to the surface, and blows them into the nest that he has constructed out of froth and bubbles.

know how sticklebacks behave during courtship. The male stickleback stakes out his territory early in spring. While protecting the territory against other males, he digs a shallow pit somewhere inside it. He sucks sand into his mouth while standing practically on his head, then turns, swims away, spits out the sand, and comes back for more. In the pit he builds a nest out of threads of water plants.

When a female enters his territory he swims in a zig-zag in front of her. If she is ready to be courted she at first remains stationary in the water with her body curved upward at tail and head, and when he swims to the nest she follows. The male then puts his mouth

3

4

close to the nest entrance to indicate it to her, and she pushes past him into it. While the female stays with head out of one side of the nest, the male nudges at her body near the base of her tail. This stimulates her to lay her eggs. After spawning she swims away and the male enters the nest to fertilize the eggs.

When male sticklebacks are ready to breed, they develop red coloration on the underside of their bodies. Females do not change color but their bellies become swollen with the masses of eggs they are carrying. When a male stickleback is presented with a crude model that is moved up and down before him but has little resemblance to a real male fish except that it has a red underside, he attacks it just as he would attack a rival male. Offered another model, this time with a swollen body shape, he swims before it in a zig-zag pattern, courting it as if it were a potential mate. By the use of many such models it has been possible to discover how a male recognizes a female. Only the swollen body—and movement—seem to be essential.

A specific stimulus or group of stimuli that can cause instinctive behavior to take place is called a *releaser*. We shall shortly return to this subject at greater length, for the discovery that there are stimuli which act in this way has thrown new light on our understanding of instinctive behavior.

Newts are salamanders that are born in water, mature on land, and return to water to breed. The courtship behavior of newts is particularly interesting because, as amphibians, they live a large part of their lives on land but have to return to the water to breed. In their courtship, just as in that of many fish, tail beating plays an important part. We saw earlier that when a male cichlid approaches a female he beats currents of water at her with his tail. These currents are sensed by the female through her lateral line system. There are remnants of this system on the bodies of newts—and thus they too can sense water movement.

In spring, before the newts return to water, the males of some species take on brilliant coloration. The male crested newt, an Old-World species, develops a bright orange underside with black spots on it as well as growing a ragged-edged crest along his body. A

The male crested newt (above) develops a black-spotted orange underside coloring and a wavy crest during the mating season. In courtship (below) the male (1) stands close to the female, flicking water at her with his tail, then leaps and turns (2) so that his tail is near her head. He now moves forward slowly (3) and deposits his white spermatophore (4). As she passes over it, the female picks up the spermatophore in her cloaca (5) and the male, his task completed, turns and swims off.

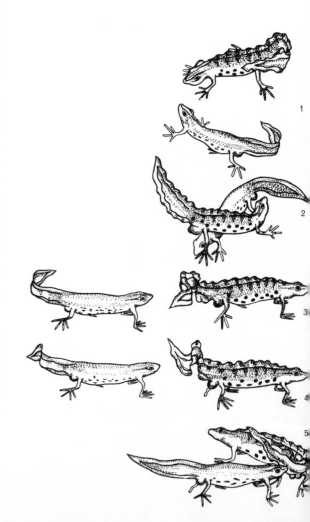

smooth newt does not have a crest but it does have the brilliant underparts. When a male sees a female, he approaches her and stands facing her head. He turns his tail round against his body, on the side nearest the female. By flicking his tail he sends a stream of water against the female's head. If she is not attracted she quickly swims away. But if she is attracted she moves slowly forward. As her interest grows, she moves ever more slowly until she stops. At this point the male leaps up, turns in the water, and lands in front of her with his tail bent horizontally across his body and held just in front of her nose. He becomes almost rigid but manages to move forward very slowly, step by step. The female follows him, her nose barely touching his tail. Suddenly there appears below the male's cloaca, between his hind legs, a small white sack-like object. This is a jelly-like bag containing sperm — the *spermatophore* — which he deposits on the bottom of the pond. He continues moving forward, drawing the female after him until she moves directly over the spermatophore. As she does so, the sides of her cloaca appear to stretch out and grasp the spermatophore, which disappears inside her. The male newt now seems to sense that his part in the mating ceremony has finished, for he swims away almost immediately.

Releasers and Imprinting

Just as each part of a male stickleback's dance leads the female to "reply," and her reply leads to the next stage, so it is with newts. The female is first attracted by the male's tail-beating performance. When she comes to a stop, he starts the next part, leading her forward and over the spermatophore he has deposited. All the stimuli that bring about the successive stages of courtship are *releasers*.

There are releasers that come into play in the courtship of certain insects. And in some cases they have been analyzed by using models, as have the releasers that operate

The diagrams and photograph show stages in the courtship of grayling butterflies. After they have danced around each other in the air the male leads the female to the ground, where they face each other with wings in the vertical resting position. Then the male swings his wings forward (bottom diagram) and holds the female's antennae between them. The antennae brush against scent scales on the wings and the scent acts as a releaser on the female, who then allows the male to mate with her.

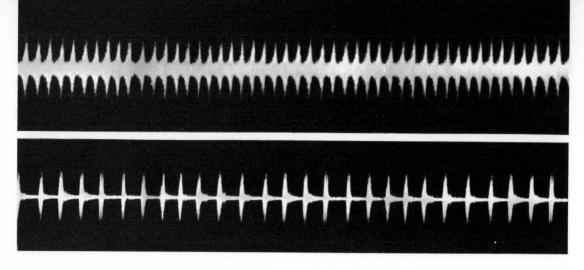

"Calls" emitted by an insect vary according to their purpose. These oscillograms show (upper picture) the normal song and (lower picture) courtship song of a grasshopper.

with sticklebacks. Perhaps one of the most thoroughly studied insect courtships is that of grayling butterflies, a species common in England. The male graylings on the ground fly to follow a female when she flutters past. After they have danced around each other in the air for a while, the male leads the female down to the ground. How does he distinguish her from another male and from female butterflies of different species? Experiments have shown that a male will fly up to a model cut out of a flat sheet of paper, when the model is moved through the air above him. It seems to make little difference whether the model is shaped like a butterfly's silhouette or whether it is just a round disk. What is important is the way it moves through the air. If it is moved up and down as it goes along it attracts more

males than if it is drawn along smoothly. Still more males are attracted if it is twisted around as it moves. So here it is the movement that serves as a releaser. However, it should be noted that none of these models attracts as many males as a real female does.

Once on the ground, the male stands facing the female. He first holds his wings above his body in the usual butterfly manner, then he swings them forward over his head. In this forward position they come to lie outside the female's antennae, which he then grasps between his wings. Swinging them back again he uses them to stroke her antennae, making contact with them at just those places on his wings where there are scales that produce male scent. After doing this several times he mates with the female. Here scent is at work

These models of correct shape and wing markings have helped identify the specific visual stimuli that attract the male silver-washed fritillary butterfly to the female during courtship. The wings of the model on the left could be made to flutter but not to close in the vertical position so that part of the wing surfaces were always visible except from front and rear. The model on the right, with rigid wings, rotated on its longitudinal axis; thus at moments during each rotation, the model was almost invisible from above, below, or either side, as well as from front and rear. The much greater attraction of the rotating model suggested that the male responds to just such a rapid alternation of color and "non-color" provided by the female opening and then closing her wings in flight. The models on the opposite page confirmed this.

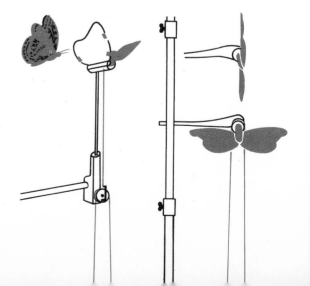

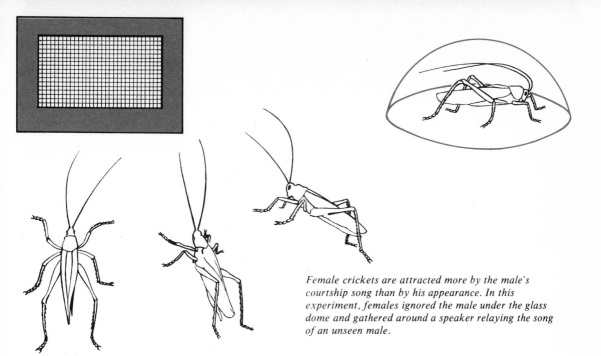

Female crickets are attracted more by the male's courtship song than by his appearance. In this experiment, females ignored the male under the glass dome and gathered around a speaker relaying the song of an unseen male.

as a releaser, causing the female to accept the male.

Sounds may also act as releasers as they do in the case of bird song. A male English robin will attack not only at the sight of red feathers but also at the sound of any bird singing aggressively on his territory. In insects, too, sound may play a part in courtship. The males of several species of grasshoppers are known to sing duets in fields, gathered together in a sort of "glee club." Their songs do not come from the throat, like those of birds. Instead, they make their noises by rasping one part of the body against another. Most grasshoppers move their hind legs up and down against their wings. On the inside of the broad upper joint of the leg is a row of pegs, which catch on the wing and set it vibrating

in somewhat the same way as a violinist sets the strings of his instrument vibrating when he draws his bow across them.

Crickets may move one wing case against the other to produce a sound. Cicadas use a vibrating membrane to make the ringing sounds that seem to set the whole surroundings in vibration. The membrane is drawn inward, then released to twang back into place. At a high frequency this becomes a penetrating noise.

The grasshoppers' song brings the males together and makes them audible over some tens of yards. The females are attracted by all this singing, and when a male sees a female he changes his tune to a courtship song, different, even to our ears, from the one he used in concert with the other males. This song lures the

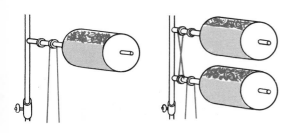

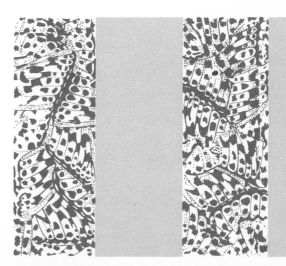

Rotating drums (above) quite unlike the shape of the female proved that the male silver-washed fritillary responds primarily to the rapid alternation of color and non-color. The drums were covered with bands (right) in which stripes made from the wings of females alternated with stripes of a neutral color. The larger the drum the greater was the male's attraction to it—an example of a supernormal stimulus.

female so that she permits the male to mate with her. Here, then, the courtship song is acting as a releaser.

Just as the songs of different species of birds differ, so do the songs of different species of grasshoppers and crickets. Singing bands are made up of males of one species only, and only females of their own kind are attracted by the song. It is typical of releasers that they are quite specific to a single species, and affect the behavior of that species and no other.

This is not to say that the releasers encountered in nature are necessarily the best. Indeed, experiments have shown that artificial releasers sometimes prove more effective than the releasers to which an animal normally reacts. One scientist studied the releasers that attract the male of the silver-washed fritillary butterflies to a female. He made a sort of merry-go-round edged with small drums that rotated as the apparatus went round. On the drums he stuck various colored patterns, including a copy of the pattern on the females' wings. This pattern proved more effective in attracting males than did any other pattern previously tried. But when he covered a drum with plain orange-yellow matched to the color in the wing pattern, this was even more attractive. The butterfly does not come across such a large patch of orange-yellow in nature, yet it was more effective as a releaser than the natural patterns. The very existence of such releasers, which are called *supernormal stimuli*, shows that some animals are, at least, capable of responding to change in a stimulus to which they normally react, even without any basic change in their behavior.

Many species of animals seem to be born with the ability to react to a particular type of releaser. But it is clear that in some way or other they learn to add details, so that they ultimately react only to one specific releaser of that type. Young unmated female crickets, for instance, will come to a telephone that is transmitting the sound of males; but females that have mated seem to have a finer appreciation of what a male should sound like, and are not taken in by the distorted sound coming through a telephone. Their repeated experience of hearing the sounds of males makes them more discriminating.

An inexperienced animal may be more easily taken in by experimental models than an experienced one. Young male cichlids isolated from a school of other young cichlids at an early stage are easily deceived by models of females. But males that have lived with a school will accept only an actual female fish. Their visual experience of their companions has enabled them to distinguish between live females and models.

Young birds that are able to leave the nest and run about freely as soon as they hatch from the egg will frequently attach themselves to the first moving object they see during the first few very sensitive hours of their lives. This is called *imprinting*. Normally, the first moving object they see will be the mother bird. Thus goslings, for instance, will normally follow their mother in a flock. But if the young are hand reared they may see a human being before they sight another bird. The result is that they will follow the human being, just as a gaggle of geese will follow their mother. The

Imprinting is a special kind of learning in which an animal develops a strong attraction toward the first moving object it sees after it is born or hatched. Usually this object is its mother, as in the case of the buffalo calf (left). Since survival in the wild may depend upon a young animal keeping close to its mother, imprinting is especially important to species whose young are able to run about within minutes or hours of being born. This applies particularly to many bird species. On hatching, the goslings (right) were deliberately imprinted on Dr. Konrad Lorenz and thereafter followed him rather than their mother.

effect of what they see during this period when they are particularly impressionable often affects them for the rest of their lives. If a gosling first sees a goose, it will choose geese as flock companions, and a goose (or gander) as a mate. But if it happens to have been a human being that has made the first impression, the young bird will try to flock with human beings and will even attempt to court one when it becomes adult.

Konrad Lorenz, the Austrian behaviorist, tells how a jackdaw that was imprinted on him tried to feed him in the same way as jackdaws feed their mates when they are courting. It could not have been pleasant for him to be plied with regurgitated earthworms by a persistent bird!

The process of imprinting, then, seems to be a way of learning to react to releasers for courtship and other behavior. In many animals the importance of imprinting is unquestionable, and indeed it seems to be important with human beings as well. Child psychologists put great stress on the importance of establishing a bond between mother and child early in life, which amounts to imprinting.

One doctor has suggested that such imprinting may have its beginnings even before birth. He has discovered that recordings of human heartbeats when played to babies soothes them more than a metronome beating at the same rate, or even soft music. The reason for this may be that while the baby is in its mother's womb it is imprinted to the sound of its mother's heartbeat. Thereafter, perhaps, this sound spells comfort and security to the baby.

This mandarin drake (below) attempted, without success, to court a female mallard. His behavior was a consequence of his being imprinted on a mallard duck soon after he was hatched.

Instinctive Behavior Patterns

Instinctive behavior—such as the courtship patterns of birds, mammals, and fish—that is triggered off by releasers is the same when performed by any animal of a particular species. There is little or no individual variation. This suggests that the behavior is not learned, but inherited. If it were learned, different individuals would almost certainly behave in slightly different ways, since it is unlikely that they would all learn in exactly the same manner. It follows from this that such behavior is probably inherited. When the instinctive behavior first appears, the basic pattern is perfect and does not require practice. We know, however, that the early experience of an animal can sometimes affect apparently unlearned behavior. In these cases it is only the outline of the behavior that is inherited, and the details, or additions to the basic pattern, are filled in by learning.

Scientists today divide instinctive behavior into three principal phases. First, some sort of internal change, such as hunger or the production of sex hormones, causes the animal to develop a drive—to feed, to reproduce, and so on. Secondly, the animal begins what is called *appetitive behavior,* that is, the search for the right conditions in which to satisfy the drive—a search in which experience and learning may well play a part. Thirdly, the animal encounters the particular releaser that triggers off the instinctive act.

Behavior that has been started by a releaser may continue after the releaser has disappeared. The more an animal has been prevented from carrying out a particular action the easier it becomes for the action to be released. For example, a male newt that has been unsuccessfully courting a female may suddenly go through the whole of his courtship behavior even though the female has taken no need of him and has wandered off. In spite of the fact that no potential mate is present he may take up the leading position, move forward, and deposit a spermatophore.

Indeed, the drive to feed or to court may become so great that the behavior suddenly takes place without any apparent releaser at hand. For instance, flycatchers may go through the action of hunting flies, or a crossbill may carry out the motions of tearing open a pine cone, though fully fed and having no need to find food. This behavior may occur even when there are no flies and no pine cones to be had. Because these actions take place without any apparent need and without any apparent stimuli they are called *vacuum activities.*

Often it is not possible for the animal to complete the behavior pattern. This can happen when a female disregards a courting male or when an aggressive male finds that his rival is not intimidated. Under these conditions, the male may abruptly switch to another, apparently unrelated pattern of behavior. For example, when ignored by the female he is trying to court, a mallard drake may turn his attention away from courtship and start to preen himself.

Over and over again we find evidence of releasers, and support for the view that they touch off instinctive behavior. The strongest evidence comes from the study of fish and birds, whose behavior is very largely instinctive. But we cannot ignore the fact that these things operate in animals more closely akin to ourselves, and that we, too, have our share of instinctive behavior.

"Vacuum activities" are forms of behavior that occur without any apparent need or stimulus. A possible example is that of stone tossing in the small-clawed otter of Malaya (left). Unlike its American relative, the Malayan species searches for food only with its paws. Sometimes, however, it will pick up a pebble in its mouth and toss it (as here) as if to make the pebble behave like living prey. Then, although the otter may not be hungry, it will go through the motions of trying to catch and eat the pebble.

The term "displacement activity" is sometimes used to describe a response that seems irrelevant to the stimuli that evidently brought it about. A male oyster-catcher, seeing its reflection in the mirror (top), at first responds as if to the presence of another male. When it looks round the side of the mirror (center) the "other" bird has vanished. It responds to this situation by preening its feathers (bottom).

Among animals whose patterns of behavior are acquired largely by experience, there is a long period of parental care and supervision while they grow and learn how to find food and defend themselves against predators. In the case of elephants this period lasts for several years. The three-week-old elephant in these pictures is crippled in its right foreleg and receives constant attention from its mother during their long daily trek for food in Northern Rhodesia. Right: The mother helps her calf up a slippery river bank. Above: The calf is made to rest before they resume the journey. Since mother and calf lag behind the rest of the herd another adult female helps guard the calf against lions.

6. Bringing Up the Young

In many species of animals, reproduction is accomplished without the parents ever seeing or having anything to do with their offspring. Sea animals such as sea anemones and sea urchins, discharge their eggs and sperm into water. Fertilization takes place there and the young larvae float about in the surface layers, settling on the bottom only when they are fully grown and ready to change into adults. No care is given either to the eggs or to the young. Right from the start the young have to fend for themselves and, as we might expect, a great many die before reaching maturity. This process of reproduction is wasteful, for very great numbers of young ones must be produced in order to ensure that enough will survive to prevent the species from dying out.

Offspring fare better in cases where one of the parents chooses a suitable place in which to put the eggs. Usually it is the female who does this, and her choice of a place for the eggs may involve a change in her normal pattern of behavior. In the ordinary way, a female cabbage white butterfly, when feeding, is strongly attracted to yellow and blue colors,

paying no attention to green. But when she is ready to lay her eggs her color preferences alter. She then finds a green leaf and drums on it with her front legs, patting it first with the left one, then with the right. In some way that we do not yet understand this seems to determine whether or not she uses the leaf as a place to deposit her eggs.

A female newt is equally careful in choosing where her eggs are to be laid. She sniffs the narrow leaves of water plants, probably selecting those that are most actively producing oxygen. When she has made her choice she maneuvers the leaf until it comes to rest near her hind legs. Then she lays a jelly-covered egg on it and uses her hind legs to fold the leaf. The jelly sticks the two halves of the leaf together to form a protective covering for the egg. The female great crested newt sometimes folds a long narrow leaf many times, accordion-wise, placing an egg in each fold.

For both the cabbage white butterfly and the newt, parental care ends with the newly laid eggs. They leave the eggs and never visit them. Yet their behavior offers some protec-

Many insects, once they have laid the eggs, have nothing further to do with their offspring. After burrowing a nest in sandy soil this digger-wasp paralyses one or more caterpillars, which she carries to the nest. Then she lays an egg on one of the caterpillars and flies off, leaving the emerging larva to feed on the captive prey.

tion for the eggs and an immediate supply of food for the young when they are hatched. Some species of solitary wasp ensure a food supply for their young by attaching their eggs to a fly or a spider that they have previously paralyzed. Other solitary wasps return to the hole in which they have walled up their eggs and feed the larvae as they grow. But once the larvae have turned into pupae, they too are abandoned by their parents.

For animals whose behavior is largely instinctive—animals that are hatched out complete with all their behavioral necessities—very limited parental care of this kind may be sufficient. But animals that have to acquire a great deal of their behavior by learning are necessarily dependent on their parents during the period of their education. In general, the more complicated the behavior of an animal is, the longer the period of parental care it needs. Many birds are hatched out with their behavioral patterns complete, but there is a period during which education by imprinting is important. Further, the young cannot de-

velop completely in the egg because it does not carry a sufficient store of food, so there must be a period after hatching when development is completed. Most young mammals, too, need time to grow and come to maturity after they are born, though the time required varies widely from one species to another.

Some mammals bear young that are able to do everything for themselves almost immediately, while others have quite helpless young. Human beings, who have to learn an extremely large part of their behavior, come into the latter category.

Among both birds and mammals the need to provide a period of care for the young is associated with some very complicated behavior patterns.

Nesting and Caring for Eggs

Nest building is sometimes an essential part of bird courtship. Though the actual building of the nest may not start when the birds begin to court, the existence of a suitable nesting site is necessary to stimulate the flow of the hormones that "fuel" the reproductive drive. At this stage some birds make no more than a scrape on the ground, while others use a wide variety of nesting materials such as grasses, bits of wool, mud, and twigs. The methods of nest building vary greatly from species to species, and a few of these methods have been studied in detail.

One of the most complicated nests is that of the weaver birds. These birds live in great flocks in East Africa. They nest in large numbers in trees which may be pushed down by the weight of nests and birds. Each nest is a beautifully woven pouch made of grass that is laced and knotted together by the birds. Weaver birds do not have to learn how to make these nests. The elaborate behavior involved, including the holding of the grasses and the beak movements necessary to thread and knot them, is thought to be instinctive.

The building of elaborate nests is not confined to birds. The sewing ant, a pest of coffee plantations, also weaves a nest. A group of five or six ants will stand on the edge of a leaf, reach out and grasp another leaf in their jaws and draw the two together. Then other ants arrive, carrying larvae. The silk that the larvae produce is now used to sew the leaves together, for the larvae serve as living shuttles, and are passed back and forth across the gap until the two leaves are securely bound together. The ants appear to be co-operating, and when enough leaves have been joined together the entire colony moves into the "house" that has been formed.

Most insects and reptiles leave their eggs to hatch unaided, but after a bird has laid its eggs it usually incubates them. One exception is the bush turkey of Australia, which puts its eggs into a pile of rotting leaves that gives off heat as it decomposes. In effect, the eggs are being kept warm in a compost heap. Most birds, however, keep their eggs warm with the heat of their own bodies. Feathers molt from an area of the hen bird's breast, and this area, called a brood patch, becomes especially well supplied with blood vessels and is therefore warm. The mother settles herself down so that the brood patch fits over the eggs, making an efficient incubator.

On occasion, eggs may be accidentally

The eggs and newly hatched young of many bird species are particularly vulnerable to predators. Weaver-birds of East Africa protect their young against tree-snakes and other enemies by making enclosed nests that hang from branches of trees and can be entered only through the narrow tubular opening at the bottom.

These sewing-ants construct nests by sewing — or, more accurately, gluing — the edges of leaves together with the sticky strands of silk produced by their larvae. The larvae are passed across the gap between the leaves until the latter are joined by a thin web of silk.

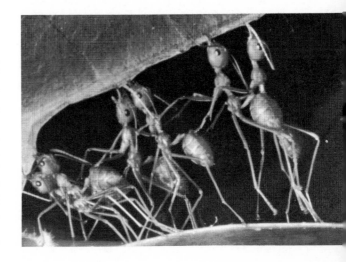

kicked out of the nest. This can easily happen to birds that make only a shallow nest on the ground. A goose makes a particular motion with her head and neck that enables her to roll the egg back into the nest. Stretching her neck, the goose places the underside of her beak on the farther side of the egg. Then she turns her beak down so that her head is at right angles to the neck. By arching her neck upward, the goose can then move the egg toward her body which is on the nest. This movement is quite instinctive, but parts of it are variable. Without a certain amount of variability the movement would not be efficient, because an egg is not a perfect cylinder, and is likely to slip sideways as it is being rolled. By moving the beak slightly to one side or another these side slips can be counteracted. These small variable movements are additions to the main instinctive retrieving pattern.

What is there about an egg lying outside the nest that causes a bird to recognize and retrieve it? Experiments with herring gulls show that they will retrieve cubes or spheres of wood, particularly if they are the color of a herring gull's egg—that is, having dark mottling on a green background—although egg-shaped ones are retrieved more frequently. So the releasers in this case are correct shape and color. Size is not important. However, size must play some part, because a model egg, six times life size, proved more attractive to the gulls than real eggs. This is an example of a supernormal stimulus, explained in Chapter 5.

While a bird is incubating its eggs it cannot leave them unattended long enough to find its own food. Either the male and female must take turns brooding, or else the male must feed

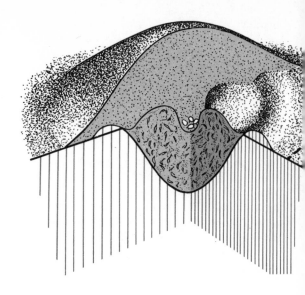

The mallee fowl of southern Australia incubates its eggs by laying them in a 15-foot-wide ground nest (shown in cross-section, above) made of fermenting vegetation covered by loose soil. The male is highly sensitive to temperature changes. The eggs need to incubate at about 92°F., and he constantly removes or adds quantities of the soil layer in response to fluctuations in the rate of fermentation and the temperature of the air.

Below: Herring gulls "retrieve" any one of these imitation eggs if it is placed next to their nest. Color, not shape, releases this retrieving behavior. Size is also significant; a model of correct shape and color, but six times as large as normal, proves even more attractive than a real egg—an example of a supernormal stimulus.

the female. A female hornbill walls herself up in a hole in the trunk of a tree where she incubates her eggs and looks after the young. During her self-imposed imprisonment she is fed by her mate through a small hole, which is her only communication with the outside world. Among most species of birds, however, male and female take turns sitting on the eggs. This is not always easy, for when a bird is sitting it reacts aggressively toward any other bird that approaches the nest. Before the sitting bird will leave the eggs, the other one has to behave in a way that will subdue its aggressiveness.

This gives rise to what are often elaborate nest-relief ceremonies. When a grey heron male alights on the edge of the nest, the female makes a great noise and stretches her neck upward. The two birds then stand beak to beak, making a kind of shouting noise. The male, edging into the nest, bends his head, raises his crest, snaps his mandibles, and eventually settles down on the eggs. Soon the female departs.

In some species the ceremony involves present-giving. In the turnstones—sandpiper-like birds that nest in arctic regions—the male drops a small pebble near the nest. When a female is ready to leave the eggs she picks it up and shows it to the male. Then she places it in the nest among the eggs and departs. Blue-footed boobies, which nest on the west coasts of Mexico and Central America, pass bunches of seaweed back and forth between them before changing places.

Some fishes, too, care for their eggs, but this is not always the work of the female. Female sticklebacks play no part in rearing the young. As with nest building, this task is left entirely to the male. He guards the nest

Nest-relieving ceremonies help to subdue the aggressiveness of the brooding bird, which would otherwise attack any bird (including its mate) that approached the nest. Above: In the gannets' ceremony the pair bow toward each other several times. The relieving bird in this picture is completing a bow, while its mate raises its head in a "flight-intention" movement prior to leaving the nest. Below: Gentoo penguins also bow toward each other. The left-hand drawing shows the relieving bird initiating the ceremony. In the right-hand drawing the sitting bird has risen and is also bowing; in a moment it will step back from the nest to make way for its mate.

containing the fertilized eggs, now and then fanning water over them by moving his fins and vibrating his tail. This drives well-oxygenated water through the nest, replacing the stagnant water that would otherwise accumulate around the eggs. As the eggs develop, the male spends less and less time fanning water at them, but if they are replaced by a batch of newly-laid eggs his fanning activities increase again. It seems clear that stimuli from the eggs themselves are releasing the fanning behavior. It may be these stimuli are chemicals whose strength decreases as the eggs grow older, and no longer stimulate the fanning behavior.

Feeding the Nestlings

Most young fishes are capable of feeding themselves, but when young birds are hatched the parents, in most cases, must feed them. This activity often keeps both the adult birds occupied throughout the daylight hours. Newly hatched thrushes are blind and helpless. A light tap, however, made on the side of the nest makes them open their beaks wide and point them upward. Such a tap is, of course, just the disturbance that the parent birds make when alighting on the edge of the nest with food, and it serves as a stimulus to prepare the young thrushes for feeding.

In some birds the stimulus works the other way around as well, emanating from the young bird and stimulating the parent bird to give food. In such species the inside of the nestling's throat and mouth is highly colored. The sight of the brilliant scarlet or yellow markings in the lining of the young bird's throat stimulates the parent to regurgitate the food into the youngster's mouth.

As the nestlings grow, their eyes open and they can see their parents. Instead of blindly pointing their open beaks straight upward, they now begin to gape in a more specific direction, toward the parent bird perched on the side of the nest and toward the parent bird's head. What is the stimulus that brings about this behavior, which seems at first glance to be instinctive but may, in fact, be learned? Experiments have shown that a simple model cut from heavy paper will serve in place of an actual bird. When such a model was placed on the end of a stick and moved

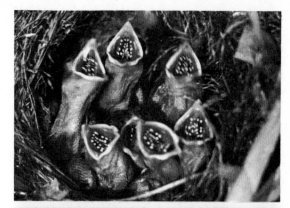

Many newly hatched birds are stimulated to gape for food by the disturbance made when the parent alights on the nest. Being still blind, the young bearded tits (upper picture) gape in a general upward direction; the older song-thrush nestlings (lower picture) can see their parent and their gaping mouths point directly toward its beak. In both cases the vivid throat colors of the young act as the releaser for the parent's feeding behavior.

Young herring gulls make the parent regurgitate food by pecking at its beak. Tests with head-and-beak models (right) have shown that this pecking behavior is released by the long, thin shape of the parent's lower mandible and the red spot near its tip, the spot being the pecking "target."

about near the edge of the nest, the nestlings gaped toward the smaller of the two circles attached to the "body". But when the size of the "body" was altered they gaped toward the larger circle, which they had formerly ignored.

The reason for this seems to be that the second circle now bore the same size relationship to the larger "body" as the first circle bore to the smaller one. Relationships of size are often important in recognizing a stimulus, and in this case the relationship between the size of the "body" and the size of the circle was the major factor in recognition. Positional relationships are also important. Young birds will even gape at a stick, provided it is held over the nest, and if two sticks are put there they will choose the lower of the two.

Young herring gulls make their parents regurgitate food for them. This they do by pecking at the parent bird's bill, which is yellow with a red spot near the tip of the lower mandible. This behavior must be inborn, because even a recently hatched and apparently inexperienced chick pecks the exact spot on the parent's head that will cause the food to be produced. It will peck also the right spot on a model. The model need be no more than a silhouette, mounted on the end of a stick and moved close to the chick.

By using a number of models and watching how often the chicks peck it has been possible to analyze exactly what it is about the parent's head that acts as a releaser. Tests with models bearing spots of different colors showed that a red spot produced the most responses — four times as many as a model with no spot at all.

The color of the model's "bill" itself made little or no difference to the number of responses except when a red one was presented; this produced twice as many responses as "bills" of any other color.

The chicks reacted even to a very distorted model of a head, though they were more responsive to distorted "heads" in natural colors than to those in other colors. Even a stick with a red tip, without any resemblance to a head, released the chicks' pecking behavior provided it was presented vertically in front of them. This again indicates that it is often one particular feature of a releaser that is all-important. Indeed, a releaser is somewhat like a caricature in the sense that both depend for their effect on accentuating one or two outstanding features.

In young birds, feeding is quickly followed by defecation, the nestlings depositing packets of feces in the nest. As these packets are white they would soon make the nest conspicuous if they were allowed to accumulate. But the parents patiently collect and remove them. When they are older, the nestlings go to the edge of the nest to let their droppings fall over the side.

Mammals and Their Young

Unlike birds, mammals do not need to go through elaborate performances such as nest building, incubating, and nest-relief activities when rearing their young. Even their courtship is usually a relatively simple and rather hurried affair, although human beings are an

A giraffe cleans the birth-sac fluid from her young a few minutes after its birth. Among many mammals this vigorous licking stimulates the young to take its first breath.

exception to this general rule, since they frequently make it a very elaborate ritual. Among mammals, once a youngster is born it is looked after almost exclusively by the female. In some cases the father may get food for the family, as the male wolf does, but even so he can be of little help until after the young ones are weaned.

Yet although she is the sole provider for her young, the mother mammal does not always know instinctively what to do at the birth. It is common, both in zoos and with domestic pets, for the mother to need help with her first birth for she is not interested in the young as much as she will be on later occasions. Per-

Right: Young mammals have to learn how to find the nipple in order to obtain nourishment. Most cattle and other ruminants feed standing up; the young instinctively search in the angles formed by the cow's legs and belly, but they must learn to choose the hind-leg angle instead of the foreleg one. Newly born piglets show suckling behavior as soon as their noses touch an object. At first, piglets fight for individual nipples, but gradually each establishes its right to a particular nipple.

haps in nature the young mother is helped by imitating the older mothers of the herd. In either case it does not seem that she finds the new born animal in itself naturally attractive.

She licks the secretions that precede the birth, and she also licks the fluid that comes from the birth sac, when the young one is born. This licking extends to any objects lying near her that are covered by the fluid, and since one of these objects is the newborn animal, that, too, gets her attention. By her energetic licking the mother cleans the youngster and also massages it, thereby stimulating it to breathe. Mother mammals sometimes take drastic action to make their babies take the first breath. For example, Californian sea-lions bear their young on land but dunk them deep in the water to stimulate them to breathe. Porpoises are born below water and the parents push them to the surface to take in their first breath of air.

Many newly born mammals are quite help-less. This is particularly true of marsupials, the pouched animals, whose young are born at an even more immature stage than those of other mammals. A young kangaroo is carried about in its mother's pouch, attached to the nipple, for as long as four months before it starts to eat grass. But the very helpless and tiny baby kangaroo somehow has to get into the pouch. Some mother kangaroos pick up the young between their lips and carry them to the pouch. Others have been seen to lick a path through the fur of their belly to lead the blind, crawling youngster into the pouch. Yet others give no help at all. Because this be-havior varies it is thought to depend upon the mother's previous experience.

Newly born kittens, like many other young mammals, are unable to urinate or defecate without their mother's help. It is entirely due to her licking and stimulation that they are able to rid their bodies of waste products in the first few days of their life. Without her attention they would die. It may seem strange that the young are unable to do these necessary things instinctively and without help, but the behavior both of the kittens and of the mother cat may have originated from the danger that would arise if a lair were allowed to become conspicuous because of fouling. In the wild state it is certainly safer for the mother to collect the excrement and keep the lair clean, in much the same way as the parent bird clears the nest of droppings from its young.

Young mammals must suck the mother's nipples to obtain the milk they need, yet the ability to find the nipples seems to be a matter of experience. Among hoofed animals that stand while being suckled, inborn behavior is limited to searching in the angle between the mother's belly and her legs. Sometimes they

choose the angle just behind their mother's front legs instead of just in front of her back legs. The mother then pushes them into the right position, and very soon they learn where to go.

Kittens soon establish a claim to a particular nipple, but before they have learned to do so their mother has confined them at feeding time in such a way that they cannot avoid searching for her milk in the right place. She will leave her kittens for an hour or so while she feeds. On her return she wakes the kittens, and then settles down, enclosing them in an oval formed with her body and legs. This restricts their search to the underside of her body, and so aids their learned feeding behavior. Kittens that have been hand-reared for a period do not know how to suck when returned to their mother.

The extent to which young mammals can be left alone without their mothers, varies a great deal. Young rabbits and hares can be left for long periods without being suckled and licked. This is an obvious advantage to the parent animals, which depend upon speed to get away from predators. They would be considerably handicapped or endangered if they could not move far from their young ones.

Some mammals, like most birds, make nests for their young. Rabbits make theirs of grass lined with hair which the female plucks from her body. Toward the time of birth the hair on the parts of the mother's body that she can most easily reach becomes loose and can be easily plucked. Deermice make nests beautifully woven of grass and set high off the ground on corn stalks. Gorillas and chimpanzees may make platforms of twigs set in the trees, sometimes with a rough roof to keep out the rain, and use them as temporary homes.

Right: In mother-substitute experiments infant rhesus monkeys invariably rejected the wire model in favor of the softer, more "mother-like" model covered with toweling. The feel of the "mother" was more important to the monkeys than food; they drank from the bottle fixed to the wire model only if they could still cling to the soft one.

Mother Substitutes

The mother's presence is undoubtedly a great comfort to a young mammal. This has been strikingly demonstrated by observing the effects of providing young rhesus monkeys with substitute "mothers." The substitutes were of two kinds, one being a wire frame fitted with a simplified non-realistic head, and the other similarly made but covered with soft cloth. Even when the baby monkeys could get food from a feeding bottle attached to a wire "mother" they still preferred the cloth-covered one, and spent hours clinging to it.

Although they like warmth, they would leave a warm pad to go to the cloth "mother," even when she was unwarmed. The contact stimulation they got by straddling the cloth dummy was evidently reassuring, for when they were startled by some strange object they did not run to the wire "mother" from which they had received food, but to the cloth one. In a room full of unfamiliar blocks, boxes and toys, the young monkeys huddled in a corner. The presence of a wire "mother" did not reassure them, but the presence of a cloth one made a great difference. The youngsters clung to it for a while, then became bolder and began to leave the "mother" and explore their surroundings.

Young monkeys reared with cloth "mothers" remained attached to them after they had grown up. The attachment formed in these cases seems similar to imprinting in birds, and it is interesting that monkeys put to cloth "mothers" at the age of eight months showed an interest in them at the time but formed no long-standing attachment. Imprinting also occurs in certain other mammals. For example, young hoofed animals will follow the first moving object they see after they are born. This is usually the mother and in this way they learn to follow the herd.

The longer the period of infancy, the greater is the importance of the bond between mother and young one, and the more elaborate is the behavior by which parents care for their offspring. And the longer a young animal is relieved by parental care from the necessity to feed itself and fend for itself, the longer time it has to learn new patterns of behavior.

The young of many species of higher animal learn some kinds of behavior by imitating the actions of their parents. Sharp claws help this mature lion to catch prey. Although his three-month-old cubs are too young to hunt food they are already imitating his claw-sharpening behavior.

7. Sources of Behavior

An animal seems to acquire its behavior in two main ways: some it inherits and some it learns. The nature of inherited behavior—which includes what we have called instinctive behavior as well as such things as reflexes—depends on the pattern of nerve cells in the nervous system. This pattern is determined by the genes that the young animal has received from its parents. Learned behavior may be defined as behavior that has been modified as the result of experience. The behavior that an animal learns is not passed on to its descendants by means of inherited genes.

Very often instinctive patterns form the core of behavior while learning adds refinements. Chicks, for example, peck for food soon after hatching. The movements of pecking—the downward thrust of the head, the upward lift, and the swallowing—are all inherited actions. At first the chick tries to pick up all kinds of things, such as small stones, marks on the ground, and even other chicks' feet. Gradually it learns to restrict itself to grains of corn and other bits of food. In its pecking movements the young bird is behaving instinctively, but the ability to apply these movements skillfully and only when they are of use is learned.

It frequently happens that a young animal is equipped with instinctive responses that it may direct quite unsuitably at a wide range of objects that show only the broadest similarities. As we saw in the previous chapter, a newly hatched bird will follow anything that moves, whether it is an old box, a human being, or another bird. This is because movement, the one quality that all these things have in common, acts as the releaser for the young bird's response. Imprinting then determines what the young bird will finally follow, thus adding discrimination to the original unselective behavior. Normally young animals become imprinted on their parents and are thus able to recognize and respond to members of their own species.

In some cases, though this is not common, a young animal is equipped with a very restricted instinctive choice that later widens. The feeding behavior of young cuttlefish is a good example. When newly hatched from the egg, cuttlefish will grasp only at a small shrimp called mysis, or at models that are very like it. These particular shrimps are the main food of young cuttlefish, but adults have a wider diet, which includes crustaceans that are shaped quite differently from mysis. In this case the animal learns by experience to broaden its choice rather than to restrict it.

Learning to Live in a Society

Apart from learning how to feed and to do whatever else is necessary to maintain its own

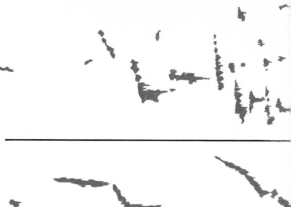

Among some bird species each individual learns trills and other elaborations on a specific inherited song from other birds in its area. Such local songs may differ from place to place. Above, left: The western (upper) and eastern (lower) meadow lark look almost exactly alike. Both species nest in the central United States but they do not interbreed, probably because their songs (shown in the spectrograms above, right) differ considerably.

life, the young animal may have to learn its relationships with other members of its society. On the whole the social mammals, such as baboons and prairie dogs, are lenient with their young, giving them what psychologists call a "permissive" upbringing. In other words the parents allow them to do more or less what they like within very broad limits, and they are not involved in the complex dominance relationships that affect the older members of the group.

A similar leniency of upbringing occurs among many species of birds. The young are not treated aggressively until their plumage is changed to adult color. Nevertheless, a certain amount of discipline is imposed on young animals. Among monkeys an old male howler has only to give one short sharp bark to quell a group of noisy youngsters.

The process of learning who is "family" and who is not is a slow one. In the early weeks after a prairie dog pup emerges from the burrow, he spends much of his time bothering the adults to groom him. At that stage, all the adults in the neighborhood group, as well as his own parents and his litter mates, will do

so. He enters other burrows and may spend the night with the families that occupy them. Even when he enters the territory of other groups he is not attacked. Indeed, he is rarely so much as rebuffed. Even when he tries to suckle adult males, they merely turn the occasion into a grooming session. It is probable that all these youthful encounters help him to build up a picture of the group with which he must later work out adult social relationships.

For as the prairie dog pup matures, hostility to his invasions of other territory begins to appear and steadily intensifies. This teaches him the boundaries of his own territory. At about this time, he starts to give the territorial call, standing on his hind legs and almost jumping into the air with the intensity of his efforts. Unfortunately he does not yet know that he should do this only on his own territory, but the reactions of the adults soon show him that he must keep his call for his own home ground and not use it elsewhere. So, before long, he finds that his own territory is closing round him. He begins to use the kiss, described in Chapter 4, to distinguish friend from enemy, and he will bark at an intruder if his greeting is not returned in kind. At this early stage he has not yet learned the tail-raising ceremony that adults employ in such encounters. This will come a little later. But by the end of a year he is educationally an adult, though not yet sexually mature.

Young baboons play in groups under the protection of adults. In their play they perform various adult activities in a somewhat sketchy way. Educational play of this sort is common, particularly among young mammals. When a kitten plays with a piece of string, her preparation to spring and the pounce imitate the movements of the adult cat when stalking a bird or a mouse.

It is important that a young animal should learn to give the same recognition signal as the rest of his species in the area, otherwise all sorts of misunderstandings might occur later. Birds of the same species, for example, must recognize each other by their song. Thrushes and most other song birds instinctively sing the right song, but the chaffinches of Europe inherit only the basic song for their species. Thus when they are raised out of earshot of other chaffinches, they sing only the basic song. When they are raised where they can hear other chaffinches they learn various trills from their neighbors, and fit these into the basic song. It then becomes the full song of that area. In some other area the chaffinches would have heard, and learned, a different variety of trills. Local variations of the species song are somewhat like local dialects in human speech. The fact that they exist shows what a large part learning plays in the songs of some birds.

Inheritance of Behavior

So far we have seen examples of animal behavior that is learned, but what can be said about the inheritance of behavior? In our present state of knowledge, the honest answer is "not much." The study of inheritance is most productive when we are concerned with clear-cut characteristics that are such as color of fur, length of limbs, color of eyes, and so on. But when we try to measure differences in behavior that result from breeding experiments we face a far more difficult problem. This is because most inherited behavior is probably the result of several genes acting to-

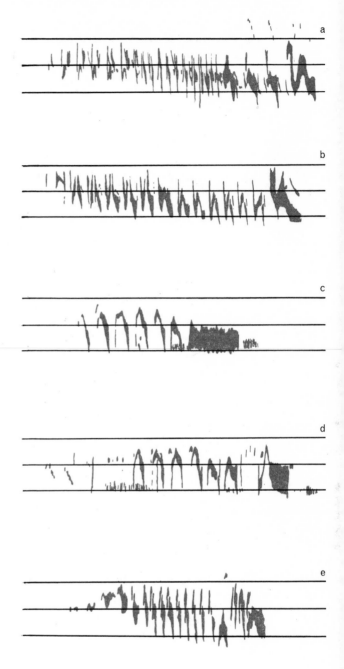

Chaffinches of Europe are one of the bird species whose calls consist of variations on an inherited song. The spectrograms above show the songs of two chaffinches used in experiments: (a) and (b) are two characteristic songs of a captured juvenile; (c), (d), and (e) are those of another chaffinch hand-reared from the age of eight days; (c), its first song, was short and simple; (d) and (e) are elaborations the bird developed after it was exposed to the songs of wild chaffinches.

gether. This combined genetic activity makes it extremely difficult to analyze the results of breeding experiments. Nevertheless, such experiments have yielded some information.

Experiments with lovebirds provide a good example. One species, the peach-faced lovebird, makes nests of pieces of grass or bark, which they tuck under their feathers to carry to the nest site. In captivity, they will tear strips of paper and insert six to eight of the torn bits among their feathers. Certain other lovebirds transport their nest material in their beaks. They, too, tear paper into strips. The hybrid offspring of this mixed parentage can tear the paper strips quite well (an activity shared by both their parents), but they are quite unsuccessful when they try to tuck the strips among their feathers. Almost every strip drops out. From the first they occasionally carry the strips in their beaks, and after three years this becomes the main method of transport they

employ. Yet even when using their beaks, they still fluff out their feathers ready for tucking.

In the hybrid the two patterns of inherited behavior clash, and the birds are unable to act in some intermediate way that would combine or efficiently adapt the two ways of behaving.

How then do different sorts of inherited behavior evolve? Such behavior is probably influenced by the same factors that bring about evolutionary changes in other animal characteristics. And we know that evolution depends on the interaction of two processes: (i) variations in inheritance—that is, differences between inherited characteristics of members of the same species, and (ii) natural selection, whereby members of a species whose characteristics are best suited to the environment will be the ones most likely to survive and perpetuate themselves. Since survival is a constant problem and adaptation and varia-

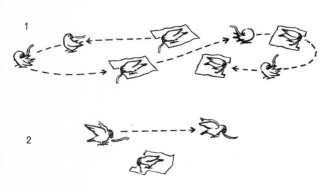

The diagrams illustrate experiments on the inherited behavior of love birds. Offered a sheet of paper as nesting material both peach-faced and Fischer's love birds tear the paper into strips. The peach-faced love bird carries the strips to its nest by tucking them between its feathers (1); Fischer's love bird carries them in its beak (2). A hybrid, the result of mating the two species, shows confusion as to which carrying method to adopt. In (3) the blue lines from A to B and black lines from A' to B' indicate the number of separate activities the hybrid needs in order to bring two strips to the nest. Success is achieved only when strips are carried in the beak—a method which it may take the hybrid three years to perfect (4). Although its feather-tucking efficiency also improves, this method of carrying strips is never successful.

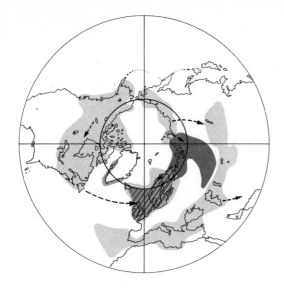

The map shows the distribution of three species of gull that probably originated from a single species around the Bering Sea. Adaptation to different environments has led to differences between these species in both appearance and behavior. In northern Europe, where two of them overlap, they behave as different species and do not interbreed.

tion are constantly occurring, we can understand that behavior patterns making for efficient feeding and reproduction will strengthen. But, at present, we can only guess how these patterns are passed on.

Other Sources of Behavior

With some behavior patterns, marked similarities enable us to make an intelligent guess at their derivation. For example, the aggressive posture taken up by a male stickleback at the boundary of his territory is very like his behavior when he is digging the pit for a nest. On both occasions he "stands" with head down and fins and tail beating vigorously, though only when aggressive does he also raise his sharp ventral spines. In discussing displacement behavior we saw that a thwarted animal may act in some way that is unrelated

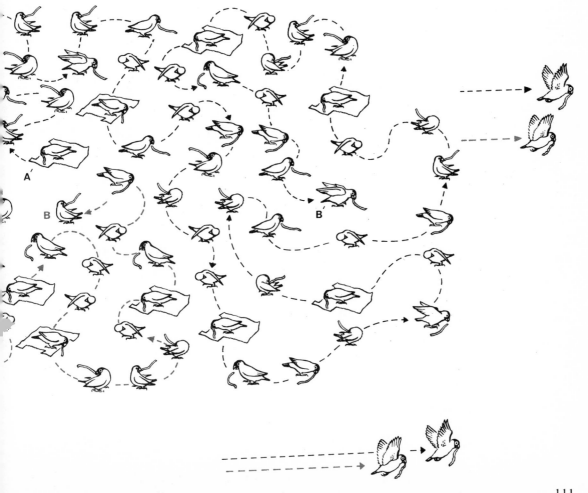

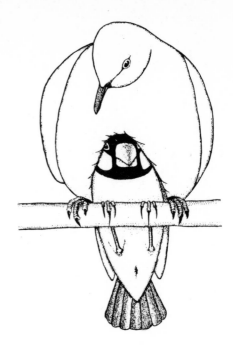

to the action it had set out to do. A stickleback in such a situation, when it is torn between attack and retreat, may displace its behavior by using its energy for digging. It is likely that in some way the digging posture becomes connected with being undecided at the territory boundary, and ultimately develops into the main aggressive gesture. But we do not know just how this becomes incorporated into the *inherited* make-up of the animal.

Another source of behavior is the natural movements of an animal. If some part of these ordinary walking or swimming movements should become a signal to other animals, let us say of alarm, then it could become a releaser for a particular kind of behavior. This may well be the origin of one of the signals that a cichlid fish gives in ordering the school of young fish to gather round it. This signal is a quick turn of the body accompanied by a raising of the dorsal fin, a movement that is normally used to change direction in ordinary swimming. This swimming movement has somehow been ritualized so that it serves as a releaser for the gathering behavior of the young fish.

A similar sort of explanation may apply to some of the courtship behavior of birds and mammals. One of the effects of hormone activity in a bird is a change in the position of the feathers. When, for example, the result of hormone activity is a greater production of body heat, the bird's feathers will be raised to allow air to circulate among them and cool the skin. If these hormone activities always accompany a particular kind of behavior, then the feather raising, which is merely a side effect, may become a signal to other members of the species that the bird is in a particular emotional state. In time, an increase in the feather fluffing, and the restriction of it to areas that are strikingly colored, may develop into display behavior.

It may be that birds showing the hormonal side-effect of feather fluffing to a greater degree than others of their species have proved more successful in courtship and, thus, in producing young. If so, the advantage would tend to be perpetuated by natural selection, and a premium would be put on heightening the effect still further. Again, however, it must be stressed that the manner in which such behavior comes to be passed on from one generation to the next is still unknown.

Birds commonly raise their feathers when inactive or
cold. In some species feather raising by one bird
stimulates others to clump with it, perhaps because a
dense group of birds finds it easier to keep warm than
isolated individuals. Feather raising makes a bird look
larger and more spherical. The drawings (left) show
how Java sparrows are stimulated to clump with doves
kept in the same aviary, the size and shape of the doves
representing for the sparrows a supernormal
"feather-raised" stimulus. A dominant sparrow will
attack other sparrows that attempt to clump with its
particular dove. The first two drawings show a sparrow
clumping beside and beneath a dove. The third shows
the sparrow preening the dove's feathers.

Among some species feather-preening has become a
specialized part of clumping behavior. This pair of
avadavats confine their preening to the head and neck
feathers, which cannot be reached by their owner. The
preener's attention is drawn toward these feathers by
the sleeked position of the feathers on the rest of
his partner's body.

Porpoises are among the most intelligent of animals. This one has been taught how to bowl alongside its tank at Miami Seaquarium, Florida.

8. Learning to Behave

Much of this book, so far, has dealt with animals dependent upon inherited behavior patterns, animals that have little capacity to learn from and use their experience. In contrast with instinctive behavior, which is unalterable, learned behavior is variable and can be adapted to new circumstances.

Some animals learn more quickly than others. Earthworms and flatworms learn far more slowly than white rats, and some white rats learn more easily than others. When we set out to test an animal's ability to learn we must first know whether it has ever had to deal with the problem set by the experiment. If we use an animal that has lived in the wild, we cannot be certain what experiences it has had. For experimental purposes, then, it is much better to work with animals whose history is known right from birth. This means that experiments on animal learning are usually restricted to animals that can be easily raised in the laboratory. As a result, only a few species have been studied in any great detail. One of the animals most widely used for learning experiments is the white rat, which is an albino variety of the wild rat and has been bred in laboratories for hundreds of generations.

In learning experiments it is necessary to control the tasks the animal has to do so that its attention will not be distracted. Because of this, most learning experiments are carried out in artificial surroundings that have little to do with the way in which the animal would normally live. But care is taken to see that the test itself is not too far removed from what the animal might encounter in nature.

In addition, the experiment must be carefully planned to make certain that the experiment really tests what the scientist wants to study. The importance of this is shown by what once happened when a psychologist was testing a rat to see if it could learn to distinguish between two visual patterns. He put a different pattern on each of two doorways. By pushing one of the doors open the rat could find food, but the other door was made so that it would not open at all. This test was planned to depend on the rat's use of its eyes. But when the animal was put down in front of the doors it crept along the floor, twitching its nose rapidly and completely ignoring the patterns. It was using its nose and sense of smell. After much trying the psychologist hit on a solution. He put the rat on a stand from which it could *jump* toward the two doors. When the rat jumped at the door bearing the pattern that meant food, the door opened. The rat would go through and land on a ledge where food awaited it. The door bearing the other pattern was shut tight, and on jumping at it the rat fell back into a net below. The rat was no longer able to sniff along the floor, ignoring the patterns. It had to look before

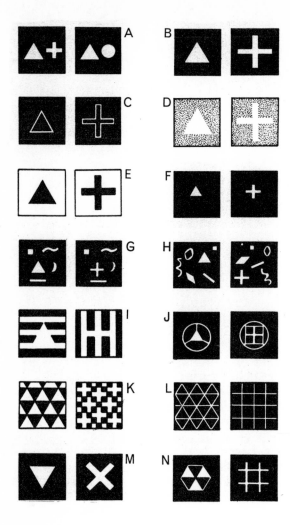

Above: In tests, rats trained to distinguish between the two (B) figures had varied success in distinguishing between the figures in the other pairs. They were successful with pairs (C), (D), (F), (G), (H), (J), (K), and (N). They failed to distinguish between the figures in, for instance, (E)—the "negative" of (B)— and in (I), where background markings partly obscured the triangle and cross figures.

Many young animals must learn to discriminate between useful and harmful features of their environment. A young bird, for instance, will often attempt to eat cinnabar-moth larvae (right) which are, in fact, unpalatable owing to some property of their skin hairs. Though its appetite for other caterpillars remains unaffected, the bird soon learns to recognize the vivid yellow and black "warning colors" of the cinnabar-moth larva and to reject it as food.

leaping. By using its eyes to detect the difference between the doors, it soon learned to distinguish between the two different patterns.

Association and Reinforcement

In the experiment just described, the rat learned to associate a particular pattern with the open door. If the door leading to food had been always on the left or always on the right, the rat might simply have formed the habit of jumping to the left or to the right. To avoid this possibility the doors were switched in a random manner. Since the door that opened switched from right to left some times and remained on the same side at others, the pattern was the only clue the rat had. This ensured that the rat could obtain food only by learning the correct pattern.

Experiments of this sort enable scientists not only to test an animal's ability to learn but also to find out what the animal can see. The illustration shows examples of pairs of patterns used to test the visual and learning capacities of rats. If a rat could not distinguish the differences between a pair it obviously could not learn to associate one of the pair with the open door.

Association is often the basis of learning. Chimpanzees, for example, soon learn to put disks of a particular color into a slot to obtain a grape, in much the same way as the rat learns to distinguish between patterns to get food. In both cases the correct action brings a reward. If, after a time, the reward is no longer offered, the animals may start making errors in choice again. They appear to forget what they have learned. The reward, seems to strengthen the association that the animal learns. A reward that has this effect is called a *reinforcement*.

Elephants are supposed to have long memories. Tests similar to those described above show that elephants also have a considerable capacity to learn to tell the difference between patterns. One circus elephant had no difficulty in recognizing the difference between the patterns shown on this page. It was rewarded when it chose one of the pair and given nothing when it chose the other. It remembered the correct pattern for 18 months, the longest period for which its memory was tested.

Some of the higher species of animals are capable of generalized learning. The rat that has been taught to select the smaller of two quite small but similar patterns will later be able to pick the smaller of two much larger patterns. It has not merely learned to associate a particular pattern of a specific size with the reward, it has learned in a general way to choose the smaller of a pair. A similar thing happens in cases where an animal has

Indian elephants are quick to learn, and those used in forestry or road building learn the meanings of more than 200 commands. Experienced elephants will often anticipate the commands of their mahout. The pair in these photographs display remarkable coordination in maneuvering a heavy log with trunks and feet.

learned to pick out the lower of two specific musical notes. Given a second pair of notes that is higher or lower than the original pair, it will still select the lower of the two.

Learning in Invertebrates

The ability to learn is not confined to vertebrates. It also appears in animals with less complicated nervous systems.

The rate at which different animals learn varies greatly, however, and among invertebrates learning is slow. Even an earthworm can learn to make a simple choice, such as whether to turn right or left. This was tested in a T-maze fitted with an electric grid in one of the arms at the "top." The worm crawled along the "upright" of the T, and if, on reaching the "top," it turned to the right, it came into contact with the grid and received a slight shock—just enough to make it turn back. But if it turned to the left it crawled into a moist dark box. This offered almost ideal conditions for the worm, and was its reward for making the correct choice. However, it took 150 attempts before worms learned to make the correct turn immediately on reaching the junction of the T. As with all species, some of the worms tested proved to be faster learners than others. When the electric grid was moved from the right arm of the T to the left, the "brighter" worms solved the problem faster than the others.

It is less surprising, perhaps, to find that insects, many of which live a highly developed social life, are capable of learning. While much of the work that goes on in a honeybee hive is the result of instinctive behavior, honeybees show considerable powers of learning at some stages of their lives. This is best illustrated in forager bees, who appear to learn not only the places where flowers provide particularly good supplies of nectar, but also the time of day at which the nectar is available. Bees, too, can be tested experimentally by giving them food-finding problems to solve. Near the end of the last century it was demonstrated that bees could learn to associate a color with a place for food and that, by this association, they would visit that color on other occasions. Incidentally, these experiments also showed that bees can see colors. A number of squares of colored paper were laid

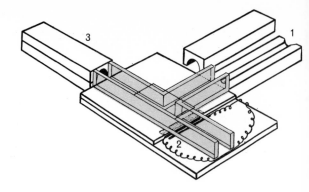

Above: T-maze used to test the learning ability of earthworms (see text). (1) is the entrance, (2) the electric grid, and (3) the dark chamber.

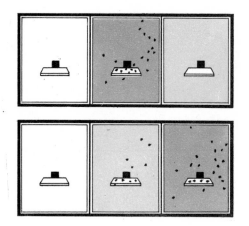

Above: Bees can distinguish between different colors and they use this ability in learning to recognize their hive and feeding places. To test this the fronts of three adjacent hives (upper diagram) were covered with metal plates painted (from left to right) white, blue, and yellow, the center (blue) hive being the only one occupied by bees. When the positions of the yellow and blue plates were transposed (lower diagram) home-coming bees went immediately to the empty but now blue-fronted hive on the right. Hive color, not position, was the recognition factor.

Right: A solitary wasp "homes" on its burrow by learning to recognize local landmarks. If a ring of pine cones is placed around the entrance while the wasp is in the burrow and then moved to one side after it has left, the returning wasp will search inside the ring for the entrance. If the cones are later heaped on one side of the entrance and a ring of black blocks is placed on the other side, the wasp will first search in the new ring. The wasp's behavior shows that it recognizes the relationships among objects, not the objects themselves.

out on a table top, and a small dish was placed on each square. Sugar water was placed only in the dishes on the blue squares. The bees were then allowed to visit the table and, of course, they found the food. After they had made several visits of this kind, all the dishes were thoroughly cleaned. There were now no scent clues from the food to aid the bees; nevertheless they still visited the blue squares more frequently than any of the others.

To make sure that no traces of sweetened water remained on the colored squares, the papers were covered with a glass sheet that could easily be wiped clean of any drips or of bees' feet marks. The papers were also shuffled from time to time to avoid any possibility of the bees alighting on certain squares merely because of their position. By eliminating these and other possibilities, it was proved that the bees truly learned to associate a particular color with the food reward. Bees can also learn to visit paper squares bearing certain patterns, but there are other patterns that they simply cannot distinguish one from another. This, however, is due to a limitation of their sensory equipment rather than to an inability to learn.

It is clear from their behavior that bees have an acute sense of position, which depends upon their learning the landmarks in their surroundings and along the way to and from the hive. If the hive is moved a foot or two to one side, or turned through a right angle so that the entrance faces a different way, the bees will fly around searching for the entrance at the place where it was at first. It takes them quite a time to adjust to the new position.

In a few cases it has proved possible to discover how animals make use of landmarks to find their way. Solitary wasps, which are fairly close relatives of bees, recognize a pattern of landmarks rather than the individual marks themselves. One species of solitary wasp digs a hole in which it places bees it has caught to provide a food store for its larva. While the wasp is stocking the hole, it makes several hunting trips, returning each time with another bee. If a ring of pine cones is arranged around the hole before the wasp emerges and then moved to one side after it has left, the wasp, on returning, will search inside the circle, although the hole is now outside it. If the pine cones are piled into a heap on one side of the hole and a circle of black blocks is arranged on the other side, a new question arises. Will the wasp visit the pine cones, which are no longer in a circle, or the circle, which is no longer composed of pine cones? In fact, the wasp most frequently chooses the circle, recognizing it as such although it is now made up of black blocks. It has learned to recognize the landmark by the relationships

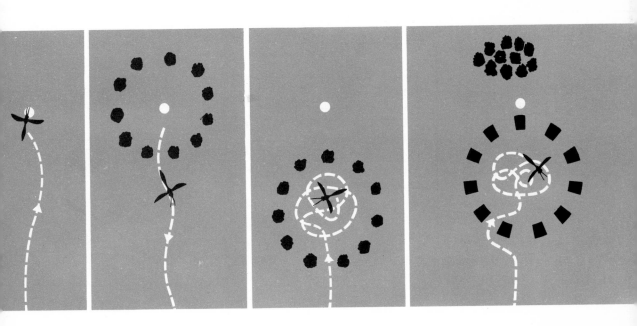

between the objects that compose it, and not by the objects themselves. This is somewhat similar to the case of the male stickleback, to whom the relationship of red coloring to the rest of the body, not just redness itself, is important as a releaser.

Learning and Brain Structure

The nervous system of an insect, though not nearly as complicated as that of man, is complicated enough to make it difficult to trace what happens there when it learns. If we wish to understand something of the connection between learning and the actual structure of the brain, we must turn to some animal whose brain structure we can at least begin to unravel.

One such animal is the octopus. It is a relative of snails and clams, but possesses a far superior nervous system to theirs, and has a proved ability to learn. An octopus will settle down in a tank fairly soon after being transferred there from the sea. If stones are put in one end of the tank, the octopus will make its home among them. When a crab is dangled at the other end of the tank, the octopus will glide out from the stones toward the crab, seize it, and eat it. If, every time a crab is presented, the experimenter also presents a white plastic square, and moves the square around near the crab it will not be long before the octopus will come out for the square alone. This shows that it associates the square with the presence of the food. If a piece of white plastic of a different shape is also put into the tank and wired to a battery so that it will give a mild shock when touched, the octopus soon learns to come out for the white square and stay in its home when the second shape is presented.

After an octopus has been trained in this way, part of its brain can be removed to see how this will affect what the animal has learned. When the vertical lobe at the top of the brain is cut off, the octopus can no longer retain anything it has learned by means of its eyes. Before the operation it may have been able to remember the shapes and their associations for several days. After the operation it will remember for only two minutes before it begins making mistakes, and the mistakes will continue to be just as frequent in spite of practice. This indicates that the vertical lobe must play an important part in memory. In the octopus, it seems that memory may be related to changes in the connections of the nerve cells in the lobe. When the lobe is removed the long-term memory store is no longer available.

Similar attempts have been made to locate the area in a mammal's brain where learning is carried out or "stored." We associate a mammal's power to learn with the development of the *cortex,* which is a thick layer of cells covering the two halves of the *cerebrum,* the largest part of a mammal's brain. The cortex has many folds and *convolutions*

to increase its area. But there seems to be no part of the cortex particularly concerned with learning in the way that other parts are concerned with vision, touch, and so on. Damage to the cortex in rats does not affect their ability to learn or remember. Even when the damage is extensive rats can learn and remember as long as a small proportion of the cortex — and this can be in any area of it — remains intact. This seems to mean that all parts of the cortex play a part in learning and memory.

Conditioned Reflex and Habituation

The experiments that the famous Russian scientist, Pavlov, carried out on dogs show that the *conditioned reflex* has many features in common with associative learning. Ivan Petrovich Pavlov (1849–1936) was a physiologist who wanted to find out what causes the production of saliva in a dog's mouth. If a dog sees food, it salivates, just as we do. But Pavlov discovered that if he regularly rang a bell just before food was shown to a dog, after a time the saliva would begin to flow as soon as the bell was rung. Salivary secretion at the sight of food is a true reflex, but in this case the response had been transferred to the bell because it was always rung just before food appeared. This conditioned reflex could be produced only if the dog was in a sound-proof room cut off from any disturbing influences. The dog would go on salivating at the sound of the bell as long as the food was

presented. If food was not given each time, so that the dog's response was not reinforced, then the amount of saliva produced at the sound of the bell gradually decreased until there was no response at all. This blotting out of an acquired response is called *experimental extinction,* and it demonstrates the importance of reinforcement in responses of this kind.

Another example of experimental extinction is that a rat that has learned to press a lever for food will stop doing so if the food reward is withheld for a period of time. This is in keeping with the adaptive nature of learning. In the interest of the efficient use of energy it is as important to dispense with a learned action that no longer serves a useful purpose as it is to learn the purposeful action in the first place. Experiments with both animals and students in school show rewards are more effective than punishments in learning.

At one time many kinds of complicated behavior were explained in terms of the conditioned reflex; but today it is not considered to play such an all-important role as was formerly believed. No doubt conditioned reflexes do play a part in the behavior of most animals, and of ourselves, but there are other equally important aspects of learning. One of these is "learning *not* to behave," or *habituation,* as it is called. Habituation is the process of getting used to something in the environment and developing the ability to ignore it. All young animals react to loud sounds by a show of fear. Obviously, they could not even

Left: Having learned to associate a white, square shape with a crab titbit, an octopus (far left) now gets a mild electric shock when it touches another, similar shape. When crab and shape are offered again (center) the octopus approaches with caution but is shocked once more. After several shocks the octopus (near left) learns to reject all contact with crab or shape.

Right: Equipment for testing saliva-secretion conditioned reflex in dogs. (1) Source of sound or visual stimulus; (2) food bowl. Saliva runs from dog's gland down tube (3) to balance plate. As each drop falls onto plate the cable (4) carries "message" to smoked drum (5) on which frequency and amount of secretions are recorded.

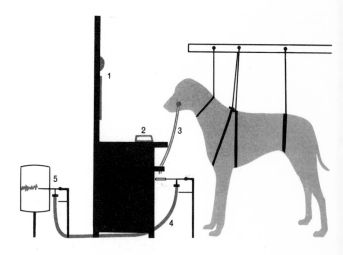

feed efficiently if they stopped every time they heard a bang. But by habituation they learn not to react as long as the loud noises are not accompanied by any harmful effects. This protects the animal against the waste of energy that would result from coming to the alert at every sound. It is believed that wild animals never habituate to their natural predators. This prevents animals from losing respect for dangerous enemies even though they may have encountered the predators several times — perhaps when they were well fed and in no mood to attack.

Learning without Reward

We have seen how important rewards are in reinforcing associative learning. Yet not all learning depends on rewards. Imprinting, for instance, seems to bring no obvious and immediate reward except, perhaps, the security the chick may experience in trailing along behind its mother. However, more and more evidence is accumulating to show that most young animals learn a great deal without any apparent reward, in the process of gaining experience of their surroundings.

Rats may be raised in cages that give them little chance to run about, or in cages where they can run about but not climb, or in others equipped with ladders, wheels, and ramps that offer a wider range of activities. Animals brought up in the last type of cage can learn their way through a maze more quickly than those brought up in the second type. Those reared in the second type do better at finding their way than those reared in the first type. Each of the three groups of animals has learned from the experience available to it, and each group appears to have learned without reward as they moved about their cages.

The experiences that a young animal undergoes are of the greatest importance in determining later behavior, and since it is impossible to rear an animal without allowing it any experiences at all, it is always difficult to be certain exactly what parts of its later behavior are inborn and what have been learned from experience. Even if a young animal is kept in a dark soundproof room so that it hears nothing and sees nothing, it will still experience the sounds made by its own body, and it will still experience the sensations of touch between different parts of its own body and between

Above: The environment in which a young animal has been reared has an important bearing on its behavior when adult. The photographs show (upper) a normal laboratory rat cage and (lower) a "free-environment" cage with ramps, tunnels, movable "toys," and abundant food. A rat reared in the lower cage, which offers a far wider range of experience, would on average be likely to have superior learning ability to another rat from same litter reared in the upper cage.

Right: The chimpanzee has little difficulty in solving the problem of reaching the bunch of bananas suspended above his head. After a few moments in which he appears to be looking over the problem, he quickly builds a tower of boxes that enables him to reach the reward. (See also the illustrations on pages 22 and 23.)

its body and the cage. There is evidence to show that a female rat must be able to lick and explore her own body while cleaning it if she is to be able to deliver her young successfully. The knowledge so gained of her own body seems to lay the foundation for this later behavior.

Animal Intelligence

A question that often arises is, what is the connection between learning and intelligence in animals? One simple answer is that many animals learn by trying all sorts of behavior and gradually discarding all but those that meet the situation to be dealt with. An intelligent animal does not need to make as many trials, since it will find the correct solution quickly, or even immediately.

Some 50 years ago, a scientist named Wolfgang Koehler studied the intelligence of chimpanzees. The problem he tested them with was to hang a banana out of reach above their heads, and then to put boxes of various sizes inside their cage. The banana was sometimes arranged so that it could be reached by climbing on one box only. The apes easily solved this problem without trial and error.

When two boxes were needed, they would try one, retire to a corner and eye the situation, then suddenly run to another box, pick it up, and place it on the first one. With this tower they were immediately able to get the banana. Sometimes, however, the solution was an unexpected one. One chimpanzee took a keeper by the hand, led him to a position directly under the banana, then leaped on his shoulders and grabbed the fruit!

The chimpanzees would also retrieve bananas from outside the bars of their cage with a stick. When the bananas were put farther out of reach, a chimpanzee discovered how to fit two sticks together, pushing one into the end of the other. On the whole the solutions the chimpanzees found for their problems seemed striking evidence of intelligence. However, chimpanzees in the wild are known to use sticks as weapons against predators and also as a means of getting insects out of holes, so it may be that these animals, not reared in captivity, were simply applying their experiences with sticks to a new situation. Similarly, earlier experience in climbing trees may have contributed to the solution of climbing onto the boxes, and even onto the keeper. Nevertheless, there is no denying that these apes

A puppy (left) and a chimpanzee (right) show marked differences in how they tackle this food-finding problem. The puppy will commonly bark, jump about, and scratch at the fence before finding a way round it. The chimpanzee goes to the food at once. The process of "seeing" the answer to a problem is called insight learning.

arrived at the correct solution without having to resort to hit-or-miss efforts.

Perhaps the chimpanzee's mental powers are best shown when a young one is brought up in much the same way as a human child. This can be done for three years or so, but after that the ape becomes so strong that an ordinary house will not hold it. However, by that time the animal will have made considerable progress.

One such chimpanzee was Viki, a female brought up by Dr. Keith Hayes and his wife, Cathy in the United States. Viki did many extraordinary things during her early years but one was particularly outstanding. One day she appeared trailing her finger-tips along the ground, for all the world as if she were dragging a toy along by a string. But there was no toy or string there to pull. This game developed, and in time Viki would pull in the imaginary string hand over hand until the imaginary toy reached her. Then she would drop it and begin to haul it up once more. There is no doubt that Viki had invented an imaginary toy with which she mimicked her own actions with a real one. Imagination on any scale is unusual in animals, and the extent to which Viki exhibited it is probably unique.

Intelligence tests show differences between individual animals very clearly. A batch of six-week-old puppies showed great differences in behavior when trying to solve the relatively simple problem of getting at food which they could see on the far side of a fence. These pups were brought up without previous experience of any such obstacles, so the problem was entirely new to them. Some of them jumped up and down, barking and scratching at the fence. Only after they had calmed down did they try to find their way around it.

Others were less excitable and almost immediately looked first at one end of the fence then at the other before going round and getting to the food. Differences were again apparent when the fence was extended at both ends. Some puppies went along the fence as far as they had formerly gone, and then yelped and scratched at it as before; again, it was only after they had calmed down that they explored farther and found their way round to the food. The calmer ones, however, immediately followed the fence to its end and ran around it. One possible conclusion is that the second group was more intelligent, since they found the right solution without experimenting with barking and scratching.

Scientists have to be careful when attributing intelligence to an animal, for they have been tricked more than once in the past. Clever Hans, a horse that was said to be able to do arithmetic problems, is a case in point. When simple problems were written on a black-board the horse gave the answers by scraping one hoof along the ground the cor-

The jackdaw in the upper drawings learned how to open the box that had the same number of dots as the "key" card on which the bird stood. The lower drawings show a more complex version of the same problem that a raven also mastered. The arrows point in each case from the key pattern to the only correct box in each group. In all cases the key cards comprised dots of different shape, size, and positional relationship from those of the "correct" answer.

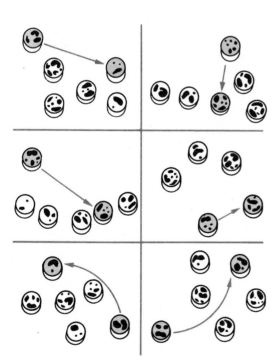

rect number of times. This seemed a remarkable feat of intelligence until it was found that if no one in the room knew the answer (because they could not see the black-board) Hans went on scraping his hoof long after he had reached the right total. The same thing happened if all the people in the room were behind a screen where the horse could not see them. It then became clear that Hans could get the right answer only by reacting to the slight movements made by his keeper, or by anyone else present, which indicated that he had reached the right total.

While waiting for the horse to produce the answer the audience probably became tense, then suddenly relaxed when the correct answer was reached. This relaxation, or possibly a slight audible intake of breath, or the merest nod was enough. The horse had learned to stop when he sensed them. Professional mind readers sometimes work in a similar way. They sense the barely perceptible reactions of the audience which indicate that they are "getting warm," and make use of these signs to give approximately correct answers that start as shots in the dark but become more and more accurate.

Although there is no proof that animals can add, there is now clear evidence that some birds and mammals can recognize numbers. Not only can they match numbers, but they can also remember them and apply that memory to later actions. Ravens, jackdaws, and parrots have been taught to take food from one particular bowl among a group of bowls according to the number of black spots on the lid. They choose the one that bears the same number of spots as a master card placed nearby. There seems little doubt that the birds really do count the spots on the card and on the bowl lids, because the spots on the card are not the same size as those on the lids, nor are they arranged in the same pattern. If the correct bowl had five spots on its lid and the master card had five spots, and if in both cases the spots were arranged in the same way as they are on the five of hearts or the five of spades, then the bird might pick the correct lid by recognizing the pattern, and not by counting.

In this experiment, a raven learned to pick out the correct bowl from among five others.

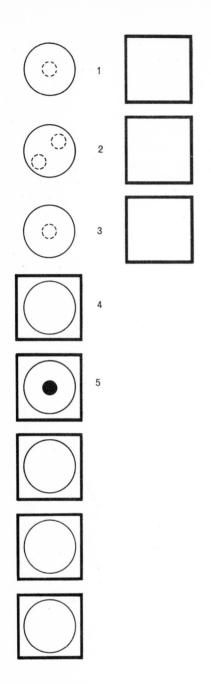

The birds were also trained to take a certain number of grains of food from bowls with plain colored lids. Some of these bowls contained three grains, some two, some one, and others none. For each experiment the bowls were shuffled so that in any particular row the number of bowls that had to be opened to obtain, say, five grains was different each time. Nevertheless, a jackdaw was trained to collect two grains if the lids were black, three if they were green, four if they were red, and five if they were white.

On one occasion this bird's behavior was especially striking. It had been signaled to take five grains of food but had taken only four, finding one in the first bowl, two in the second, and one in the third. It then went to its cage, turned around, and returned to the bowls. There it nodded its head once over the first bowl, twice over the second, and once over the third. Then it knocked the lid off the fourth bowl, which proved to be empty, and moved on to the fifth, from which it took one grain of food. Again it went to its cage, but this time, having completed its task, it stayed there.

The way in which the bird nodded once for each grain of food it had taken suggests that it was making imaginary marks—one mark for one, two marks for two, and so on. This is called "thinking unnamed numbers" and while it resembles counting on one's fingers it is different from the way in which we normally think about numbers. We think of two not as "one-one" but as a number symbolized by quite a different word and quite a different numeral sign from those symbolizing one. Yet it is doubtful whether our recognition of numbers of objects in a group is much better than that of birds. If a number of spots are projected onto a screen for not quite long enough to permit counting, most people can recognize the number correctly only up to five, though a few people may guess correctly up to eight. Pigeons can recognize up to five correctly under the same conditions. This ability appears to be a primitive one. It may well be basic to our ability to do mathematics.

Human intelligence tests are based on the same idea as the tests given to animals. These tests are based on the idea that there is some inherited basic and measurable quality of

A jackdaw, trained to take a total of five pieces of food placed at random in four out of eight boxes, took four pieces from the first three boxes and returned to its cage. A moment later it returned to the boxes, bowed its head once over the first box, twice over the second, once over the third as if recapitulating (correctly) the number of pieces it had taken from each. Then it opened the fourth, empty box, went on to the fifth, from which it took one piece, and retired to its cage, having completed its task.

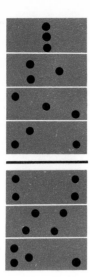

After it had learned to distinguish between a card with three dots on it and another with four dots, an elephant was able to identify the cards when the positions of the dots were changed. It could still do so after an interval of a year between tests.

human minds called intelligence. According to this idea, intelligence is something that is not changed by experience, education, or home and social background. On this assumption, a set of problems is given to children and adults of various age groups. Some children find the tests easy and others find them far too difficult. From many such tests made in the past, it has been possible to determine the kinds of questions that most members of a given age group can answer. And if a child taking the test can answer correctly all the questions usually answered by five-year-olds, he has a "mental age" of five. "Intelligence quotient," or I.Q., is found by dividing the mental age by the age in years and multiplying the quotient by 100. For example, if an eight-year-old boy answers all the questions usually answered by twelve-year-olds, his I.Q. is 12 divided by 8 multiplied by 100, or 150. Average I.Q. is 100.

It is very doubtful, however, whether such tests are measures of "pure intelligence," for it is clear that home and social background, as well as other factors, *do* affect a child's ability to solve problems.

In this experiment, food was attached to one end of a piece of string, the other end of which was tied to the bird's perch. The bird obtained the food by pulling the string upward with its beak and holding the slack with its foot. Some beak-and-foot coordination seems inborn in this bird, though the efficiency of coordination improves with practice.

Two flocks of starlings, about 30,000 in all, join prior to their autumn migration south from England. On their long journeys to and from their winter homes, migrating birds navigate by the sun and by the stars. The birds' internal "clock" enables them to hold to their correct course in spite of the sun's and stars' changing positions in the sky.

128

9. Rhythms in Life

Not all behavior can be explained either as instinctive acts triggered off by external releasers, or as actions that the animal has learned to do. Some behavior comes about without any apparent outside stimulus and seems to be initiated entirely from within the animal. This is particularly true of behavior related to natural events that occur with a regular rhythm such as the change from day to night, the ebb and flow of the tide, and the cycle of the seasons. It is true that such natural events are signaled by changes in the environment—the change from day to night by the gray of twilight, the change from winter to spring by increasing length of day, and so on. Very often, however, the behavior of animals is set in motion by processes within the animal that are apparently independent of the stimuli that come from the environment.

We all know that some animals, including most song birds and most insects, are active by day while others, including bats and owls, are active by night. It is easy to assume, therefore, that the periods of activity and rest in such animals are determined solely by the regular alternation of daylight and darkness. This is not, in fact, the case. If we keep a field mouse (a naturally nocturnal animal) under different lighting conditions for a long period and record its times of activity, we see that there

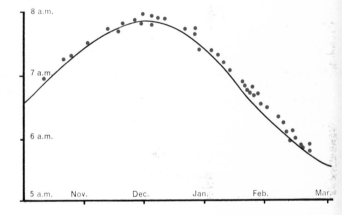

The "biological rhythm" of many animals allows them to take account of seasonal changes in the length of day. In this diagram the black curve shows the times of sunrise in Brittany, France, from November to March. The dots, which follow the curve very closely, show the times at which the daily activity of the European mole begins during the same period.

129

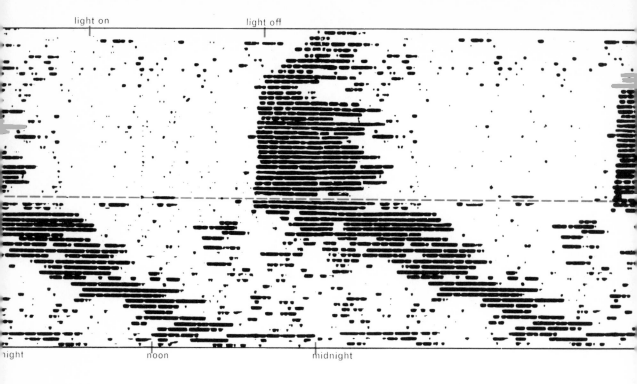

is another rhythm in operation—a rhythm that is apparently unconnected with the effects of dawns and sunsets.

The changes from night to day and from day to night are marked not only by changes of light and darkness but also by changes of temperature and differences in natural sounds. In this experiment the first problem is to determine what are the effects of light and darkness on the mouse. The experiment must be conducted in conditions that eliminate any stimuli other than light. The apparatus must be soundproofed and the temperature kept constant. If we switch on the light for the 12 hours of each day, we find that the mouse starts to be active as soon as the light goes off. It keeps going for a few hours, then gradually slackens as the "night" wears on.

If the animal is kept in constant light for a period of several days and nights it starts its activity later and later, and individual periods of activity become shorter and shorter, until finally they cease altogether. It seems that prolonged continuous light alone has inhibited the animal's activity, for if the light is at last switched off and the mouse left in constant darkness, the activity begins again. Now the mouse is in continuous darkness, and each

period of activity is approximately as long as it was while the mouse was living in 12-hour periods of light and darkness. But the gaps between active periods become longer and longer. In other words, the beginning of the activity period becomes later and later on successive days. The mouse's rhythm of activity and rest is now following a pattern unaffected by any external influence and is said to be *free-running*. Each complete phase of this free-running rhythm lasts more than 24 hours. So, as time goes on, the activity-rest cycle gets more and more out of step with the length of day. But when the mouse is again exposed to regular periods of light and darkness, it soon returns to starting its activity when the light goes out.

From these experiments some scientists believe that the light-dark sequence acts as a regulator for the mouse's own internal rhythm, keeping it in step with the 24-hour rhythm of the earth's rotation to which dawn and sunset are geared. Many scientists say that it is possible to compare the mouse's internal rhythms with a clock that runs "fast," while the sequence of dawn and sunset can be compared with a time signal by which the clock is set at the right time.

130

*Hormone secretions gear the activity periods of
cockroaches to the onset of darkness. The graphs below
show these activity periods (1) under normal dark:
light conditions and (2 to 5) under various experimental
dark: light regimes. Dark periods are in gray; their
duration is shown on hour scale at bottom. The blue
curve in (3) shows the activity of a "non-rhythmic"
cockroach in which an activity rhythm had been induced
by implanting a ganglion from a normal cockroach.*

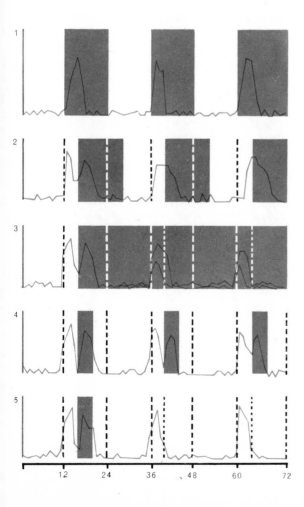

Internal Rhythms

Internal rhythms operate in both animals
and plants. In plants, for example, the rhythms
may be marked by changes in the use of
oxygen or the release of carbon dioxide. In
human beings, body temperature, rate of heart
beat, and blood pressure all vary rhythmically
in the course of each day. And the existence
of an internal rhythm in fruit flies is shown
by the fact that they emerge from pupae
mainly at dawn.

All these rhythms seem to be located within
the living organism and to be independent of
external stimulation. They also appear to be
inborn and not to be the result of learning
even though they may not always appear immediately. For instance, if fruit flies are kept
in darkness the emergence of adults from the
pupae may occur at any time, as do the activity periods of cockroaches that are reared
in darkness from the egg. Yet both of these
activities can be brought into a rhythmical
time pattern merely by submitting the insects
to a single flash of light lasting as little as
two-thousandths of a second. From then on
the regular rhythm will continue, though it
will not be synchronized with the 24 hours
between one dawn and the next, or one sunset and the next, unless the insects experience
alternating periods of light and darkness each
day.

It is not certain why a brief flash of light
should have this effect. One possibility is that
it serves to synchronize several internal
"clocks," each of which was formerly working at its own rhythm and was out of phase
with the others. As soon as all the "clocks"
work in step with each other the collective
rhythm becomes apparent.

Research done on activity rhythms of cockroaches has shown that a blood transfusion
can bring about the transfer of a rhythm. If
blood is taken from a cockroach with a regular
rhythm and put into one that has been reared
in darkness and therefore shows no rhythm,
the second one will then show the same
rhythm as the first. This indicates that at least
some part of the rhythmic behavior is controlled by hormones circulating in the insect's
blood. These hormones, which come from
nerve cells in the insect's brain, are released
into the blood at regular intervals. The hormones are released into the blood when the

131

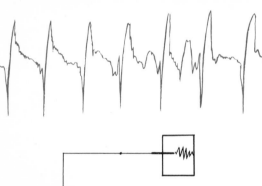

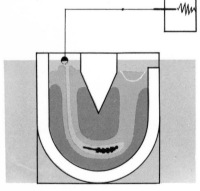

Lugworms live in U-shaped burrows on the sea shore (top), taking in water at one end of the burrow and pushing up worm casts at the other in a 40-minute activity rhythm. The apparatus (bottom) is used to study this rhythm. A float on the surface of the water in the apparatus rises and falls with the worm's activity and is connected to a smoked drum on which the activity rhythm (center) is recorded graphically.

insect's activity periods begin. When the hormone-producing cells are chilled sufficiently to hold back the hormones, activity is also held back. If the chilling lasts for six hours, activity will begin six hours later than normally.

Not all animal rhythms are geared to a 24-hour period. Some are much longer and others much shorter. A good example of the short-period rhythm occurs in lugworms, which live in U-shaped burrows in muddy sand by the sea shore. The tail end of the burrow is marked by a worm cast, a twist of sand expelled from the worm's body. The head end of the burrow is marked by a slight dip in the surface where the worm has sucked in sand and where water has drained in. The water is used for breathing and is passed through the burrow by the worm's movements. If a worm can be made to burrow in sand that is held between two glass plates, its movements are indicated by changes in the depth of water over the burrow. A float on the surface will move up and down with the water level, and by means of a lever resting on a slowly rotating smoked drum "the worm writes its autobiography," as the English zoologist G. P. Wells has said. The illustration shows the line traced by this method during several hours of such a recording.

It is clear that every 40 minutes or so, with great regularity, the worm moves to the tail end of the burrow to push out its gut contents, thus adding to the worm casts. Then it passes back to the bottom of the burrow where it vigorously pumps the water toward the head. This regular 40-minute cycle of events cannot be sparked off by any external rhythmical happening, because in the laboratory, where such experiments are conducted, there are no tides and the time the light is left on may bear no relationship to the length of day and night. Again, the rhythm appears to originate within the worm. Part of its gut, near the front end, seems to act as the pacemaker for these cycles, for this part, even when it has been removed from the worm, still continues to contract with the same rhythm.

Rhythms Geared to Tide and Moon

Land animals, whether they feed by day or by night, commonly have activity rhythms that are closely in step with the 24-hour cycle of dawn to dawn, or sunset to sunset. But there are many marine animals whose feeding times are limited by the state of the tide, which undergoes two complete cycles in little more than a day. Many shore-dwelling shellfish for example, can feed only when the water covers them. It is a great advantage for such animals to be able to anticipate the arrival of the water so that they can make the fullest use of the limited feeding time available to them. It is not surprising that many of them have a twice-daily rhythm, feeding when the tide is high.

There are also certain animals that can spawn only when the state of the tide, or the moon, or both, is right. A well-known example is the palolo worm, which lives in coral reefs in the Pacific Ocean. At breeding time palolo worms grow an extension to their bodies that becomes filled with either eggs or sperm according to the sex of the animal. At certain times of the moon, during October and November, this extension breaks off and swims to the surface of the water. The eggs and sperm are shed into the sea and the covering, having fulfilled its job of transport, dies. Millions of these worms, all geared to the same rhythm, may spawn at the same time, and a considerable area of water is then made white with the eggs and sperm. These are good to eat and the natives of nearby islands make a holiday to scoop up masses of the delicacy.

Another striking example of breeding rhythms geared to moon and tide is found in the grunion, a little fish that spawns high up on beaches along the west coast of United States at the times of new and full moons from March to August. At these times tides rise unusually high, and the egg-carrying females together with some males allow themselves to be carried far up the beach just before the tide recedes. There the females burrow into the sand and deposit their eggs, which are fertilized by the males. While this is going on,

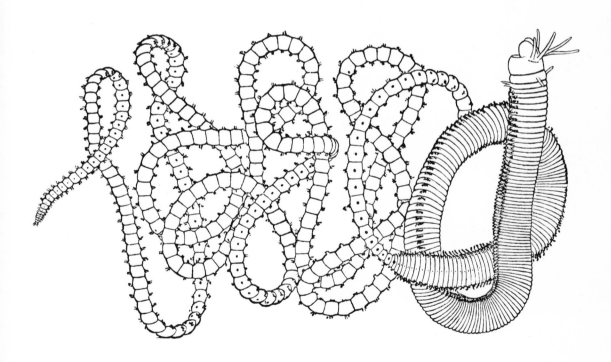

Palolo worms of the South Pacific shown here spawn during the last quarter of the moon in October and November, when the 10- to 15-inch tail extension, filled with eggs or sperm, breaks off from the rest of the worm's body and swims to the surface.

Many other animals besides the palolo worm have internal rhythms that are geared to the rhythms of the seasons. The quelea, one of the African weaver-birds, constructs its intricate nest only after the onset of the spring rains which lead to an abundance of fresh, pliable grasses that provide ideal nest-building materials.

the tide has receded, and the grunion are stranded until the next wave rolls in. They flop back into the surface and struggle back into the sea, leaving their eggs in the wet sand.

If the fish have chosen a time, as they usually do, when the highest tides are over, then the tides that follow will not come as far up the beach, and their eggs will remain safely buried until the next period of very high tides, about two weeks later.

Though the eggs develop, the young fish do not hatch until the next very high tides disturb the sand. The exceptionally high tide then acts as a stimulus and millions of tiny fish emerge, to be carried out to sea as the water retreats. This sequence of events involves a number of timing factors. One of them, probably, is an internal rhythm that brings the adult fish into a reproductive state. The actual hatching of the eggs, however, is dependent upon the external rhythm of the tides.

A Rhythm Geared to the Year

There is a rhythm, geared to the length of year, that brings birds into reproductive condition. The bodily changes that end in the fertilization and laying of eggs can be divided into three stages. First is recovery from the loss of breeding ability that follows each season. Second is the production of hormones that cause, among other things, the formation of the sperms. And third is the bursting of eggs from the ovary into the oviduct and their fertilization.

The first stage does not seem to be affected by the environment, for even birds that are kept out of sight of normal daylight conditions and isolated from seasonal temperature changes will undergo this stage. The second stage, however, is highly dependent upon environmental conditions. Outside the tropics the annual return of lengthening hours of daylight is the major influence in carrying it through. Under natural conditions a particular length of daylight in late winter sets off the bodily changes, although unusually low temperatures may retard them. In the tropics, the arrival of the annual rains, instead of the annual return of lengthening daylight, triggers off the second stage of the reproductive cycle. The third and final stage depends on a number of stimuli, including the availability of nesting sites and the whole of the courtship performance.

The annual cycle of reproduction begins with an internal rhythm, which, having begun the cycle, hands over control to stimuli from the environment.

Rhythms and Temperature

Investigations of short-term rhythms have revealed at least one unexpected property. In general these rhythms are not slowed down by lowering the temperature or speeded up by raising it. It is true that when an animal is cooled down to 37°F. the cycle of its activities may be held up altogether, but when the animal is warmed again, the cycle will be resumed at the point where it stopped, and will then continue as if nothing had happened. This means that under normal conditions the rhythm is independent of temperature—a property that is of great importance if the animal's activities are to remain in step with rhythmical natural events such as the tides or the alternations of day and night. If an animal's rhythm speeded up on a hot day and slowed down on a cool one, it would get out of step with the rhythm of day and night or with the unchanging cycle of the tides. These rhythms that are unaffected by temperature remind one of the motion of a pendulum, which swings at the same pace in hot weather as in cold.

Internal Rhythms as Clocks

All the evidence considered so far in this chapter points to the fact that some animals, at least, have internal rhythms that are changed very little, if at all, by varying temperatures or by the rhythms of the external physical world, even though the animals' rhythm may move at the same pace as the external rhythms. These internal rhythms seem to serve as clocks, which give the animal a way of measuring the passage of time. What advantage an animal gains from this may not, at first sight, be clear. But we know that many animals travel considerable distances and therefore need some means of navigating, usually by using the sun. Even human beings found navigating by the sun extremely difficult until the eighteenth century, when John Harrison in-

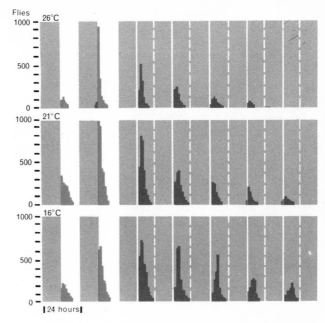

Fruit flies usually emerge from their pupae at dawn. The rhythm persists almost independently of temperature, even in constant darkness, though—as the graphs show—the rhythm lengthens slightly at 60°F. (the relationship between time and rate of emergence is in red). In these tests the pupae were in constant darkness after 48 hours of normal light:dark conditions.

To find its position when far from home a bird notes movement of sun from (1) to (2). From memory it knows that at home, at same hour, sun would be farther along its arc (2a); thus it knows it is west of home. Also, sun climbs faster between (1) and (2) than at home, so bird must be south of home. (If in Southern Hemisphere it would be west and north of home.)

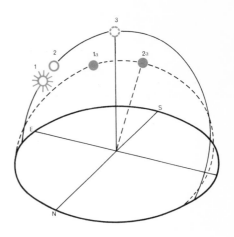

vented a chronometer capable of keeping accurate time at sea. It is easy to understand that an animal's sense of time is particularly important in finding direction and in navigating.

About 40 years ago a Swiss biologist, Rudolf Brun, while watching ants returning to their nest, placed a box over one and trapped it for two and a half hours. When he released the insect it ran off in a direction different from the one it had been following. Brun noticed that the new direction differed from the old one by an angle of about 37°. He also knew that the sun, which appears to move through a complete semicircle (180°) during the hours of daylight, had moved through an angle of 37½° during the two and a half hours that the ant was imprisoned. Brun thought that the ant was using the sun as a navigational beacon, heading out from the nest with the sun on its left and returning with the sun on its right. This is called a *light-compass reaction.*

This method of steering a course is useful only for journeys of short duration. The sun appears to move continuously throughout the day, but in the course of a few minutes the movement is through only a very small angle, so that the error made in using the sun as a beacon is also a small one. But if the journey is one of long duration, then the sun moves through a much bigger angle, and the error is greatly increased, unless the animal has some way of allowing for the sun's movement over a period of time.

Many birds, insects, and crustaceans that make long journeys, and use the sun as a navigation aid, do in fact allow for its changing position in the sky. They make approximately the correct allowance for each unit of time by using their own clocklike internal rhythms. In some cases, however, animals can make adjustments for the sun's movement by other means. Recent work with wood ants has shown that only young, inexperienced ants are misled in their direction-finding by experiments like those of Rudolf Brun. Older and more experienced ants seem to allow for the sun's changing position in the sky by using landmarks such as trees and stones.

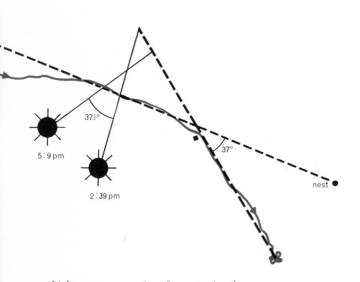

5:9 pm

2:39 pm

nest

Light-compass reaction of an ant using the sun as a navigation aid. While the ant was returning to its nest at right, a box (black square) was placed over it for 2½ hours. When released the ant proceeded at an angle to its home direction almost exactly equal to the angle through which the sun had moved while the ant was under the box.

The existence of a time sense in honeybees has been known for some time. Experiments have shown that if food dishes are filled only at certain fixed times of each day, bees learn to visit them only at the appropriate times. This timing of food gathering is important. Since some flowers give nectar only at certain times of the day, it is obviously efficient behavior for the bees to visit them only when the nectar is available. In finding her way to a known source of food, a worker bee makes use of the sun either directly, by using it as a navigation beacon, or indirectly, by noting the changing patterns of polarized light set up in the sky. When she returns to the nest, the worker informs other bees of the direction of the food source by performing the kind of dance described in Chapter 3.

The bee's internal clock—like Harrison's marine chronometer—is not affected by being moved from one part of the world to another. In one experiment, bees were trained to come out for food at a particular time in a room in Paris. Then, between feeds, they were flown to New York and placed in an identical room

that had been prepared for them. They still came out for the food at the correct moment *by Paris time,* not by New York time, which is five hours behind.

We might imagine that bees from the Northern Hemisphere could be baffled in the matter of direction-finding by taking them to the Southern Hemisphere, where the sun appears to move counterclockwise instead of clockwise. When this is done the bees are quite confused at first. Their route-finding is disturbed and their dances are upset. But within a matter of weeks their behavior corrects itself. Apparently they can learn to adjust themselves to the sun's seemingly reversed path and act accordingly, which is a remarkable example of their adaptability to new experience.

There is a species of shore sandhopper, a shrimp-like animal, that also uses the sun and has an internal clock. When the tide recedes, this animal, a relative of crabs and lobsters, buries itself under a layer of moist sand. When disturbed or driven away from its moist spot it travels toward the wetter sand

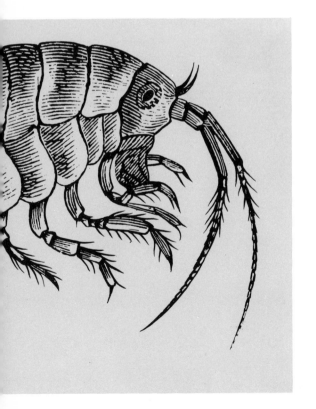

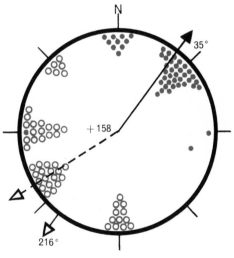

A species of sandhopper (left) has an internal clock that enables it to allow for the movement of the sun when making for the sea from its burrow on the shore. The diagram shows the result of experimentally putting this clock 12 hours "out of phase" with actual day-night conditions. The affected hoppers (blue dots) moved in a mean direction that differed by almost 180° from that of other hoppers (circles) used as controls. The direction of the shortest route to the water's edge is indicated by the arrow at 216°.

near the edge of the sea. Two Italian zoologists took some sandhoppers from the west coast of Italy, where they had always hopped westward to the sea, over to the Adriatic coast on the east, where the sea lies to the east of the beaches. Despite the change of position the hoppers still traveled westward when disturbed, just as they did in their native surroundings, although this direction now led away from the sea instead of toward it. It is clear, then, that the direction they take is not in response to the sea, its sound, or the bright light reflected from its surface. It is in response to the position of the sun. This can be proved by shading them from the sun itself and projecting an image of the sun onto them from the opposite side, with the help of a mirror. They will then turn around and hop in the opposite direction.

One thing is clear. These animals must rely not only on the sun but also on an internal clock. If they relied on the sun alone, they would always move at a fixed angle to its position in the sky. But, in fact, they always move westward, no matter what direction the sun lies in at the time. Thus they must allow for its changing position.

The sandhoppers' internal clock can be reset in the laboratory by keeping the animals in artificial "day" and "night." If, over a fairly long period, their "laboratory" dawn coincides with the time of natural sunset outside, and their "laboratory" sunset coincides with the time of natural dawn outside, they are put 12 hours out of phase with the real day-night relation. If they are then tested to see what direction they take in the open, we find that they head off in the opposite direction to that taken by animals not kept in artificial conditions. By changing the day and night relation, we have reset their clocks by half of the 24-hour cycle and their direction is altered by half of the sun's full daily circle of 360°. As a result they move in exactly the opposite direction from their normal one.

The most spectacular journeys in the animal kingdom are those taken by migrating birds. The migrations of birds to and from their breeding places have captured man's interest for many years. Almost as fascinating are the flights of certain birds that can find their way home from distant places to which they have been transported, even though they may never have visited those places before. These two kinds of journeys raise two problems. First, how does a migrating bird maintain a course? Next, how does a bird like a homing pigeon discover where it is and how to find the correct direction in which it must head for home?

It is only in recent years that we have begun to find answers to either of these questions. The less difficult one is that about the migrating bird, which we now believe maintains its course by making use of the sun and an internal clock, in much the same way as the sandhopper does. This answer came as the result of the experiments of Dr. Gustav Kramer, a German ornithologist. Many caged birds make numerous restless little flights from their perches to the bars of the cage and back again. Kramer noticed that caged starlings, throughout most of the year, made these flights in random directions, but in spring they headed eastward, and in autumn westward. These are just the directions that migrating starlings take in that part of the world during spring and autumn respectively. Kramer showed that the directions taken by the caged starlings were influenced by the sun. For, when the cages were screened from the sun, or when the sun was veiled by thick cloud, the birds' spring and autumn movements ceased to follow any particular direction and became random.

The role of the internal clock in influencing the birds' course was revealed in a different way. A starling can be taught to seek food in one of a ring of boxes arranged round its cage. A human being would find it easiest to learn to visit a box in, say, the direction of the sun at any particular moment, but a starling finds it easiest to learn to visit one that lies in some fixed compass direction — say north. In order to find the same box (and therefore the same fixed compass direction) at any time of day, the bird must be able to recognize the relationship between that compass direction and the sun's direction *at any time of day,* even though the sun's direction changes hour by hour. And experiment shows that the bird can, in fact, do that.

By keeping a starling under artificial lighting conditions it is possible to alter the time kept by its internal clock. If, for about two weeks, the light is switched on six hours before

Above: A cage for studying navigation of birds permits a bird to see only the sky. Lower picture shows the feeding boxes to which the bird is trained to go. Below: Plan diagrams of the cage show (top) number of times a starling fed at box it had been trained to choose. After a period with an artificial "day" six hours behind normal time it chose (center) the box at 90° from "correct" box. When this was followed by a period in constant illumination the bird continued to choose the "wrong" box (bottom).

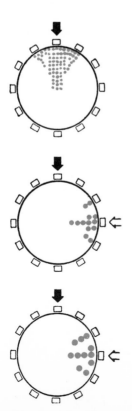

sunset, the starling's clock will get six hours out of step with the sun's daily rhythm. The bird will then have the impression that the sun has moved 90° farther in a clockwise direction than it actually has moved. Thus, if it has hitherto flown to the box that lies due north of its cage, it will now fly to the one lying due east; its normally chosen direction is changed by 90°. But if it is kept in natural conditions of alternating day and night for some 10 days, its clock will once more become synchronized with the rhythm of the sun's daily apparent movement, and it will again fly due north to the correct feeding box.

It is clear, then, that at least some migrating birds have all the necessary equipment to use the sun, in spite of its changing direction in the sky, as a means of maintaining a course. But can birds use the sun to locate their position when they are in a strange place? There is strong evidence that some can do so. Black-headed gulls, for example, when released from a strange place in sunshine, quickly take up approximately correct directions for home; if the sky is overcast, however, they are confused and fly off in all directions.

Finding one's position, as a bird must do before it can fly homeward, depends upon the use of two coordinates. Let us see how humans would solve the problem. If we can discover both our latitude and our longitude we can pinpoint our position anywhere in the world. There are other coordinates that we could use too, but most of them involve the use of compasses or electronic devices that birds do not have.

However, there is one system of coordinates that depends solely on observing the sun's position from the spot where one happens to be and comparing it with an accurate memory of what the sun's position would be *at the same moment* from one's home locality. It is not impossible that some birds can do this, especially if they have the one necessary piece of equipment—a "clock" set to their own local time and unaffected by temperature changes or changes of location. Such a "clock" would enable them, from any part of the world, to be aware of the time at their home.

Let us see how this piece of equipment could help a bird to discover how far east or how far west it is from its home. The farther west one goes, the more the sun lags behind the home sun, being lower and lower in the sky before home noon and higher and higher in the sky after home noon. Going farther and farther eastward from home exactly the opposite applies. Thus if the bird is aware of home time, and if it remembers the sun's position at that time at home, it can also be aware of how far east or how far west it is.

Judging how far north or south it is would perhaps be more difficult, but not impossible. Near the equator the morning sun climbs the sky very quickly, spends much of the day high overhead, and then, in the evening, falls rapidly toward the horizon. Near the poles the sun's path is flatter—it never rises very high overhead, and so its rates of climb and fall are much slower. Possibly a bird is able to compare the sun's rate of climb and fall, at home with the rate in regions farther north or farther south. If birds can do this, it would explain their ability to determine the direction of home.

But all this is only a possibility and not proven fact. It is possible to devise experiments to prove whether or not birds really do locate themselves in this way, but unfortunately it is extremely difficult to carry out such experiments.

In any event, no explanation of this sort could account for the way in which some birds carry on their migrating flights by night. Even if such birds take the initial direction of their night flights from the position of the sun just before it sets, they must still somehow maintain that direction during the hours when the sun is no longer visible. Experiments carried out on European warblers offer a clue to the way in which this may be done.

Caged warblers behave much the same as caged starlings. They fly in the correct migrating direction at the appropriate times of the year, and they will do so even at night, provided the stars are out. Warblers that have been reared in the laboratory, never seeing the sky by day or by night, will still fly in the correct migratory direction in the autumn if their cages are exposed to the starry night sky. However, if the moon is bright, so that the stars are less clearly visible, their direction-taking may be upset. It seems that they must use the stars as a guide. But we are not yet sure just what it is about the stars that guides them. It may be that particular constellations are important, or it may be that certain individual stars serve as signposts, or it may be factors quite different from either of these.

One thing, at any rate, is certain. The positions both of individual stars and of constellations vary according to the time of night, just as the sun's position varies according to the time of day. Very possibly birds' internal clocks permit them to allow for this varying position, and thus maintain a fixed compass direction during night flight.

There is very little that can safely be said about where these internal clocks are located within an animal's body. There is still less to be said about what they are, or whether they exist at all. To say that there are clocks even in single cells does not really tell us very much. To add that some of their properties, such as their lack of response to temperature changes, make them extremely difficult to explain on the basis of the chemistry of the cell, takes us very little farther. All we can assume is that the internal rhythms that *serve as clocks* are probably characteristic of all living things, however large or however small they may be. These internal rhythms provide springs of behavior, independent of environmental influence, that are used in many of the important activities of life.

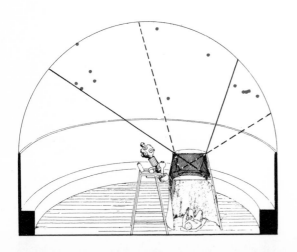

A planetarium (left), which can simulate tne positions of stars at any time of night from any point on earth, is used to test birds' capacity for celestial navigation. In map (right) the solid black line shows the migration route of the lesser whitethroat, the broken line that of another warbler. The blue arrows show headings taken by whitethroats in planetarium tests that simulated the night sky when seen from the locations of the arrows on the map. The numbers refer to those of the circular diagrams (right, below) which give a more detailed record of headings taken by the birds in the tests. In (2) the bird initially headed west after being shown a planetarium sky corresponding to a position several hundred miles east of its normal migratory starting point.

Among lower animal survival may hinge upon quite simple responses to stimuli. This animal, called a chiton, lives on stones on the sea shore. At high tide it is covered by water. When the tide ebbs and the animal is exposed to the heat of the sun, it moves toward the under side of its stone, where the surface is likely to be damp and in shadow. It remains there until the tide rises again.

10. Behavior and Survival

It is by its behavior that an animal lives, for its behavior is the means by which it adjusts itself to the happenings in its surroundings. These adjustments enable it to carry out its life activities, such as its search for food, mating, and reproduction. They also enable it to avoid extremes in its environment—heat or cold, drought or wetness—and to select the most favorable conditions from the range that is available.

This sort of *maintenance behavior* may be extremely simple, particularly in the lower animals. A good example is the chiton, or coat-of-mail shell, a relative of snails and clams, which lives on the upper part of the seashore. At high tide this animal is submerged in cold water. At low tide it may be left for as much as six hours exposed to dry air and the warmth of the sun. Yet two simple reactions, one to gravity and the other to light, enable it to avoid extremes of dryness and warmth. This animal lives on stones, feeding on tiny plants and bacteria on their surface. When covered by the tide, it shows no reaction to gravity. It moves freely around the stones in any direction, feeding as it goes. But when the tide recedes and it is no longer submerged, it reacts to the force of gravity by moving downward over the surface of a stone. Also, when the sun's light reaches it directly instead of filtering through sea water, its movements are speeded up, so that it crawls down the stone at a fairly brisk pace. As it

Tests have shown that the downward movements of the chiton shown on preceeding page are not haphazard. The diagrams show their movements when they are placed on glass sheets held vertically in air—left, on plain glass; right, on roughened glass. Movement is invariably downward in both cases, and is quicker in strong light than in weak. When the sheets are placed vertically in water, the animals move in all directions.

nears the underside of the stone, it finds shaded and usually moist conditions. With less light to stimulate its activities, it slows down and eventually comes to a stop. Not only is its behavioral need satisfied, but it has also found a good position for surviving the period between the tides.

Behavior and Adjustment to Environment

A simple pattern of behavior, then, allows the coat-of-mail shell to remain unharmed by major changes in its environment caused by the rhythmical movements of the tide. But there are many changes in environment that do not occur with any marked rhythm. There are major changes in climate that, on the whole, occur irregularly over very long periods of time; and there are sudden and unpredictable local changes, such as the complete drying up of a pond. The capacity to adapt behavior in response to environmental change of this kind is usually found in only highly evolved animal life.

Of course, an animal can be protected against changes in its environment by mechanisms other than behavior. For example, a warm-blooded animal, solely because it *is* warm-blooded, is less affected by drops in temperature than is a cold-blooded animal, whose activities may be brought to a halt. An amphibian, solely because it is adapted to live

Physiological adaptation to environment may be crucial to an animal's survival. Rhinoceroses (above) depend on water holes to meet their need of a large daily intake of water. If their hole dries up — as here, in southern Kenya — their chances of survival are slim. By contrast the kangaroo rat (below) feeds exclusively on almost waterless seeds and is well adapted to life in desert areas of the south-western United States.

on land as well as in water, is more likely than a fish to survive the drying up of a pond.

Nevertheless, behavior can and does play an important part in enabling an animal to survive changes in its environment. For instance, in open countryside the sparrow lives and nests among bushes and trees. But as human population increases, woodlands and brush may be cleared and replaced by towns. The sparrow then changes its behavior, nesting in eaves and gutters and becoming partially parasitic on human beings for its food supply. Because it is adaptable, the sparrow is able to change its behavior to meet changes in its surroundings.

The greater the variety of environmental changes an animal can deal with, the more likely it is to survive. But the ability to deal

Sparrows are one of many species of birds that have learned to adapt themselves to an urban habitat. Where once they fed mainly on crops (below) and natural vegetation, in the towns they have become partially parasitic on man for their food supplies. In the process they have lost much of their fear of humans (above).

with changes demands variability of behavior. We have seen that an animal's range of behavior depends partly on what is inborn and partly on what is acquired by learning. The first kind, the kind of behavior we call instinctive, is too inflexible to be useful in adapting to new situations. Instinctive behavior can cope with a wide variety of possible situations only if it includes a wide range of inborn behavior patterns. But it does not. On the contrary, instinct provides a minimum of behavior patterns each of which requires little or no time to be brought to perfection.

Thus if an animal is to acquire the new behavior that is needed to adjust to new situations arising in its environment, it can do so only by learning. What is more, every individual in every generation will probably have to do its own learning. For, as far as we know, behavior that has been learned will not normally become included in the inherited patterns. In cases where this may have happened we are not at all clear about *how* it may have happened; we are only sure that the process must have taken a very long time.

The main way in which an animal learns new behavior is by imitating the learned behavior of older and more experienced members of its species. Where, one by one, all members of a species living in the same locality

Some town-dwelling birds have learned how to remove metal or cardboard tops of milk bottles (above). The maps (below) show the records of such occurrences in England up to 1939 and up to 1947. The bottle-opening technique is probably based on innate behavior patterns. The initial pecking or hammering is similar to the way they open nuts, while the tearing action used on cardboard tops resembles their method of stripping bark from twigs.

have learned a new piece of behavior, we can say that the learned behavior has become included in the tradition of the species. In such cases it is often difficult to tell that the behavior is learned and not instinctive.

Only among human beings is it possible for tradition to be accumulated, preserved, and handed on by word of mouth or with the help of written records. By these means, and especially with the help of writing, the sheer amount of tradition built up has become far greater than that of any other species. Speech and writing also enable human beings to learn an enormous range of new behavior not merely by imitation but also by direct instruction. Among no other species is there any evidence that tradition can be built up by oral means or by anything akin to writing; nor is there any evidence to suggest that behavior can be acquired by oral instruction. Animal language serves mainly to express the mood of an animal. A certain noise comes from the animal when it is alarmed, another one when it is excited, and so on. But these sounds, though they may be just as effective as the gestures and postures of human beings, cannot carry anything like the same range of information as human speech. The young animal must depend on imitation and not on instruction in acquiring new behavior.

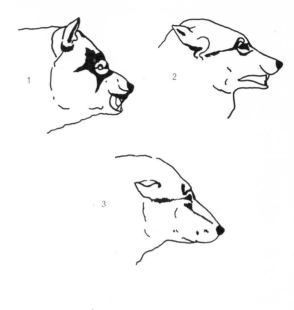

Some animals are able to communicate simple emotional moods efficiently. In the "threat" facial expressions of the wolf above (1) is of high intensity, (2) high intensity but slight uncertainty, (3) low intensity with uncertainty. Apes such as the chimpanzee below evidently find painting satisfying, for they paint readily without reward.

Behavior and Control of Environment

An animal stands the greatest chance of survival if it can not only adapt its behavior to meet new circumstances but can also control its surroundings or create its own environment to some extent. Among the few animals that can do this are termites and beavers.

The nests of termites are monuments to the behavior of these insects. They represent, in permanent form, the end result of the great mass of instinctive building behavior in which their makers have been engaged. They are ventilated by systems of tunnels that run from the base of the nest to the top. Nobody has yet made a full analysis of the behavior that lies behind the construction of the elaborate systems of passages and chambers that characterize these nests, but there is no doubt that the behavior is instinctive.

Similarly, nobody has yet made a complete analysis of the behavior that enables beavers to erect dams — dams with which they create artificial ponds, and by which they can control the water levels in times of flood. Here, however, the behavior involved shows such adaptability and flexibility that it is probably learned and not instinctive.

Again, it is in human beings that control over environment has reached its highest peak. Already we can create an artificial climate in our homes and factories, keeping temperature and humidity at the desired level,

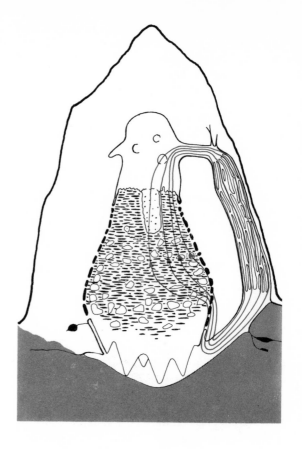

Brood chambers in interior of this termite mound surround combs of fungi that help raise moisture content. Blue lines show air circulation routes. Oxygen is replenished from outside by diffusion through exterior wall while air passes down the channels at right of diagram.

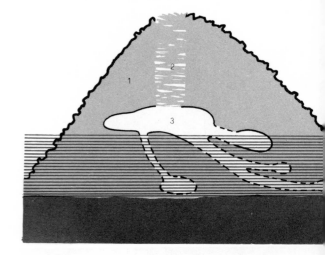

Right: In this cross-section of a beaver lodge horizontal blue lines show water level. (1) is the main wall built of sticks compacted with mud, (2) is ventilation shaft made of sticks only, (3) is central chamber just above water line.

whether the outside conditions are those of the arctic, the desert, or the tropical forest. With artificial lighting we go a long way toward turning night into day whenever we wish. With modern transport we can move food quickly from one part of the world to another, thus guarding ourselves against the worst effects of famine conditions in any particular region.

In part, at least, this mastery of our natural environment springs from our ability to amass and hand on tradition, and from our colossal range of adaptable learned behavior. In part, too, it is the outcome of scientific investigation—investigation into the happenings that occur in our natural environment and into the laws that govern those happenings. And scientific investigation of this kind necessarily includes the study of the life processes and behavior of all kinds of animals.

We have already made a start on this study, but a great deal remains to be done. In particular, we want to know more about the relationships between inborn and acquired behavior, about the mechanisms of behavior, about the way in which patterns of behavior are represented in the nervous system, and about the way in which learned behavior is stored. These are but a few of the fields open for further investigation. And, as in all scientific investigation, the more we discover the more we shall be conscious of what remains to be discovered.

The photographs (left) show an experiment made during research into the part played by certain areas of the brain in the responses of chickens to internal drives such as fear, hunger, and aggression. Electrodes have been painlessly inserted into the rooster's brain stem— each electrode being located in a section of the brain that elicits a specific response. Top picture: The rooster feeds from a bowl. Center: It receives a mild electric current in the area of its brain that elicits fear, and stops feeding to stare at an imaginary "object" that inspires its fear. Bottom: As the stimulus strengthens the rooster's fear grows until it runs away.